The juices are flowing passionately tonight, as I stir the embers within for my next steps. I thank you... from the bottom of my Soul....I'm deeply grateful for how masterfully you guided me. Lori Santo, Poet, Storyteller, Writer

The things that are FLYING into my life after my session with you made me slack jawed and JAZZED!! The opportunities before me are amazing, thank you for your wisdom, expertise and attention as I shared my vision with you! I am SO grateful! Betsy Clark, Mindset Coach

Michelle's unique take on Purpose has definitely informed my thinking and changed the way I think about Purpose and meaning. When Michelle first introduced the idea that Purpose is something that is already within us and that we can't not live our Purpose something resonated deeply with me. Since that time I've had the honor of interviewing Michelle many times both for my own programs and also have booked her on programs I produce and I have always enjoyed her insights. Doug Foresta, Podcast Consultant and Storyteller

I feel as though at last my soul voice is being heard and that makes such a profound difference. So I am deeply grateful as I felt guided to seek you out and now I know why! I feel now as though I am on my path and whatever happens, I am sharing and speaking from my heart, expressing that truth is life changing. Sara Maynard, CEO and Founder MAMS

Michelle Vandepas, from the moment we exchanged words (on FB), then actually met... you have been a plentiful source of inspiration. You took a rough ashlar, in me, and made it useful for a foundation able to support a lifetime of good & positive works. I am forever indebted to you. You are amazing at what you do. Bobbie Brooks, Politician, Activist

Praise for Purpose: The Alignment Guide

If you're done with surface explanations and methods on how to find your purpose, this is the book for you. Michelle masterfully weaves together life experience, wisdom about human nature, and an incredible toolbox of transformational exercises to support those of us on an authentic journey towards personal awakening. Read this book, and you will find deep meaning in your life and sacred connection to the truths that shape you. Joanna Lindenbaum, Master Coach Trainer

I recommend with great enthusiasm the book Purpose: An Alignment Guide by Michelle Vadepas. I work as a hospital chaplain and in a Unity congregation. I know that purpose is a huge part of well-being, and I've heard all too often how very stuck people can get when they forget their essence. And, I've been there myself. This book helps. I thought at first that this might be a book of 28 pages of easy quotes. Not at all. The introduction on purpose alone is a masterwork. The activities and questions are all designed to dig deep into the heart of the matter: which is living your best life in the pursuit of your deepest calling. Michelle Vandepas is to be commended. Pick up this book. Use it as you wish. You'll be renewed, undoubtedly. Reverand Roger Butts, Chaplain, Penrose St Francis Health Services, Associate Minister, Unity Spiritual Center in the Rockies

PURPOSE:
The Alignment Guide

28 Days of Inspiration, Reflection, Intention and Creative Expression

Michelle A. Vandepas

SPARK: The Radically Authentic Life

theSpark.love

Printed in the United States

ISBN 978-0-9724686-4-0
ISBN Ebook 978-0-9724686-6-4

Ways to Connect

**To connect with Michelle and SPARK,
Choose one or all of these ways:**

♥ Website:
TheSpark.love
Get bonuses such as coloring pages, audio meditations, guided grounding exercise, free calls and so much more to SPARK your life.

♥ Subscribe to the podcast here:
http://thespark.love/podcast/

♥ Facebook
Get support and connect with others on the SPARK Facebook group
SPARK - The Radically Authentic Life
https://www.facebook.com/groups/1296073140507882/

♥ Follow me here:
https://www.facebook.com/michelle.vandepas/

♥ Like my page:
https://www.facebook.com/michelleavandepas/

♥ Follow me on Twitter
https://twitter.com/MichelleVan

♥ Write to me, send cards and chocolate:
322 N. Tejon St. Suite 208 Colorado Springs CO 80905

DISCLAIMER

As you read through this book, know that I'm not offering therapy, coaching or anything other than advice based on what has worked for me. I'm not guaranteeing results although I've often seen them.

Please don't don't read between the lines and make up stories or think I am asking you to become either triggered or enlightened. Both of those are opposite sides of a polarity that may or may not serve you. I am not telling you to go to therapy, quit therapy, or follow my journey. I am only asking you to step into more of yourself and be brave.

You are on your journey.
Remember to listen to yourself first.
It's all inside you.
Own it.

DEDICATION

Thank you to my countless teachers, mentors, and coaches who believed in me. Thank you (I think) to all the ex'es in my life. Ex friends, employees, partners, frienemies. You've taught me through your mirror and through my pain. I honor you for the journey you've put me on.

To all my students, clients, and participants in various class and workshops: you inspire me! As every teacher knows we learn as much (or more) from our students as we teach.

Thank you to Karen Curry Parker whose friendship reactivated my soul and Camille Truman who has supported me in ways unseen for years. I appreciate you! To my editor, Heather Hilliard, who encouraged me to write my thoughts not my words. To countless more friends and teachers along the way — I also appreciate you! Thank you to Leila, (CK), Reyes whose friendship, discussion and contemplation helped plant the seeds for this book. We truly did Unleash! Thank you especially to Julia Cameron who has guided me (without knowing it) to live my own Radically Authentic Life. Thank you. Thank you to my family: my husband Bob of over 36 years, grand-teacher, daughter Kayden, my sisters Robin and Sharon, and my parents Heather and Michael, your love carries me. LAMK

Foreword

The moment of your conception marked an important, once-in-a-lifetime event. At that moment, the Universe joined your soul with a powerful story — the story of your life. The story of You is so unique that it has never been on the planet before and it will never be on the planet again.

Over the course of your life, you may have forgotten your story. You may have been told that you "should" be a certain way or act a certain way, that there are key formulas that you have to follow to be successful in life.

If you are like most people, you may have struggled to make the rules you were given fit or work for you. You may have followed the rules very well and still not gotten the results and success you wanted.

Your journey may have left you feeling depleted and not good enough. You may have lost touch with the powerful story of Who You Truly Are, which may have made you feel that there was something wrong with you.

It stands to reason that if you are a once-in-a-lifetime event in this Universe that there are no "formulas" for your success in life other than the ones that work for you. There is no one-size-fits-all approach to creating success in life. In fact, even the definition of what the definition of success is unique to each and every one of us.

In this powerful book, you're going to discover that there is nothing wrong with you. You're going to remember your own personal path back to who you truly are, and you're going to do it with the guidance, support, and encouragement of a pioneer of Purpose, Michelle Vandepas.

Michelle is one of those rare people who embrace the path that life throws at your feet with gusto and eagerness. On her journey, she's been a best-selling author, an entrepreneur with multiple million dollar businesses, a foster mom, an adoptive mom, a spiritual seeker, a business coach, and a fear-less leader.

In this program, she weaves together the wisdom of ages, different paths, various perspectives, and above all a plan for you to discover your unique way to identify what you're here to do, who you're here to be, and how to get started feeling more aligned with your authentic path.

If you browse the self-help section in any bookstore, you'll find piles of books about discovering your "type," your astrological sign, your personality profile, et cetera. Of course, these books contain vital clues, as Michelle shows you in this book.

Foreword

However, none of these books will show you HOW to make your life align with what you discover about yourself like she does. It's great to know who you are in theory. Knowing who you are can even be reassuring and affirming, but it can also leave us frustrated and overwhelmed with the prospect of figuring out HOW to live more true to who we are.

Michelle shows us that self-knowledge isn't the answer. It's just the first step and that every single step that you've taken in your life has brought you to this point — this is the moment when you finally begin to understand not only who you are, but how to live your life as yourself.

You're going to discover that you've always been doing it "right," that you haven't made any "mistakes," and that a Purposeful life is often circuitous and twisted, each turn filled with new lessons, understandings, and initiations.

The world is full of people who've forgotten their path, those who have bought into the idea that you have to compromise who you are to get along in life. When we deny who we are, our motivations and actions become silent pleas for recognition and meaning. Over a lifetime, a Purpose-less life causes us to turn down the natural light of our authentic selves, causing us to settle for lives that are grey and unfulfilling.

Michelle helps you cultivate a meaningful dialogue with your innate inner wisdom, that part of you who is restless and unsettled because you know there is more to your life than what you've allowed yourself to experience.

The exercises in this book offer you easy and instant insights into who you are and how to live on Purpose. Each page offers seeds for growth and insight that will help you craft a brave (but practical) plan to excavate the creative spark of who you are so you can add the light of who you are to the light of the world.

I can't think of a more important and worthwhile endeavor on the planet right now. I'm so grateful for Michelle's contribution.

Karen Curry Parker
Quantum Alignment System Master Practitioner, Speaker, Author, and Trainer

What is SPARK?

SPARK - The Radically Authentic Life is a life be-ing system. I created this system first and foremost for myself as a reminder to continue to go deeply into the tools that I know work. I've studied and used these for 25 years and taught them for over 15 years to friends as well as clients. I've shared these systems in workshops and retreats; I know they work. I've watched people get giant "ah-hah" moments in a quick split-second after struggling with these big questions their whole lives.

I don't expect the searching and struggling to disappear. We are human, after all, and it's part of the experience. What I do hope for you is that after using the tools in these books, you will be anchored in your knowingness, abilities, gifts, intuitions, and guidance. And that your authentic soul shines (how can your Soul be anything but Authentic?) in the following things:

✳ You understand your Purpose is a way of Be-ing, not Do-ing.
✳ You will be able and willing to speak your truth without rebellion or anger or sadness or exhalation. Just be who you are in a calm knowingness.
✳ You won't be afraid of your power, or your fear.
✳ You will be in wonder and curiosity about the world
✳ You will be able to find a moment of peace and gratitude even in the midst of storms.
✳ You will know everything is OK (even when it's not).

Each book is a 28-day journey to help you uncover and explore more deeply the focus concept of the specific book. After 28 days, allow yourself a few days of rest and integration before digging into the next book. There are nine total books, each a 28-day process and reflection so you can dig deeper into who you are and who you are growing to be. Enjoy your process.

SPARK Books:

Purpose	Mirror	Intention
Intuition	Void	Wisdom
Authenticity	Passion	SPARK

Learn more about these on theSpark.love:
SPARK Intuitive Card Deck

SPARK Cookbook

Podcast and YouTube Channel
Please enjoy the next twenty-eightdays. I look forward to loving you through to the other side.

Hugs, Michelle

SPARK Table of Contents

How (and Why) To Use This Book

There is no right or wrong way to use this book; however I do have some ideas. First, don't get stuck.

Phone a friend, get support. Skip to the activities; do what you want when you want.
Jump around. Break the rules. Follow it step-by-step, read every word.
This is your book, your journey.

Purpose is all about *be-ing* and not *do-ing.* The reason to come into your Purpose more deeply is so that the essence of who you are can emerge even more clearly. Please approach these journaling days with that in mind. There are certainly things *to do,* and you could spend an hour or more each day in this workbook, but it's not expected. You can also spend as little as 10 minutes a day and still get the full benefits. Any extra time you apply to coloring, writing, or reflecting on your Purpose will support you. Your creativity will blossom and new thought bubbles will emerge for you to explore. You can attack this book with glue sticks, colored markers, and glitter. You can also approach it with neat ballpoint pen strokes and bullet points. You can reflect quietly or dig into the papers with fervor. Some days you may do one way and other days another. There's something in here for everyone. It's all perfect for you.

There are loads of supporting materials for you. There are items on the YouTube channel as well as podcasts and other additional materials on TheSPARK.Love website. No matter where you are in your journey or how you like to approach these types of projects, honor your process. My thought is that you may work through the pages every morning, but that doesn't work for everyone. Perhaps during a lunch break or last thing before you go to bed is more appropriate for you. Maybe you'll mix it up. The most important thing is to be with the concept that you are already living your Purpose and allow that to emerge more deeply for you.

Throughout this and subsequent books, I tell you that you are living your Purpose. You don't need to go anywhere, do anything, or change in any way. It's important you follow through ideas, work through activities, spit and shine your soul a bit, and don't isolate yourself! You must share yourself with the world to feel more engaged and Purposeful (and creative).

How (and Why) To Use This Book

We live in a world of polarity, and often we swing from one side to the other — on some days there is isolation, then there are times of going out every day for weeks until we are exhausted. Some mentors and teachers talk about having balance, bringing moderation to areas of your life so they all 'balance'. I prefer to think of the balance as being in the fulcrum of the Tao where you are balancing all parts so your life because when your world is balanced, you can stay out of the polarity. This allows you to be in the center where all is possible, miracles happen, and life just is. Sometimes you'll be busy, other times not. Some days you'll eat healthily, other times not. The same swing might occur for you over the next 28 days.

Because of my viewpoint on this, you will find seemingly conflicting statements, perhaps viewing them as ideas and contemplations that come from all sides of the polarity. Embrace the juxtapositions.

Each of these books has a different theme, all leading to your Radically Authentic Life. What I mean by that is you are leading the most authentic life for you, at this moment, at this time. That may mean you're full of frustrations, or it may mean your hands are full with toddlers at home, or you have overtime at work. It may also mean you are living a life full of gardens and tea and rainbows.

How (and Why) To Use This Book

Why only 28 days? We need downtime to integrate. We have cheat days from diets, rest days from workouts and use one day for rest with spiritual reflection; perhaps you do Savasana for integration. After 28 days of using this book, you should rest, reflect, and integrate. Allow it all to swirl around inside before it finds its resting place in your body, before you move onto the next workbook.

The truth is that whichever life it is (and probably it's a combination of the two sides of the polarity), is it is the life that you're living right now. I know from experience you will feel more fulfilled in it if you are more grounded in your creativity and your Purpose. You can lead your own Radically Authentic Life in the life you already have. Some of these activities and the daily pages are here for your interpretation. It's up to you to figure out what they mean for you. We are our own best gurus.

The activities in the book will guide you to reflect, assess, and realign with the essence of your creative self. Understand that it might look differently than you'd hoped. For instance, you might not wake up at 2 AM writing words that flow from your fingertips; you may or may not end up with a "laptop on the beach" lifestyle. These processes won't make you into a thought leader overnight, a six-figure business owner in 90 days, or give you a million views on Facebook. But you will feel fulfilled, on Purpose, creative, worthy.

These different activities will bring clarity and discernment. Don't worry too much about what comes in the moment that you complete them because we are stirring up your subconscious. Write quickly when asked to do so. When possible, do not type on the computer, but use your handwriting to connect the left and right sides of the brain.

Processing the concepts, you will learn and grow into embracing the WHO of who you already are. You will sharpen the gifts that you've possessed since birth just by understanding them at a deeper level as well as acknowledge the talents and strengths you've developed along the way. You might be a visual, auditory, or kinesthetic learner; there is something in here for each of us in our alignment. It's not what you will learn in the book, but rather it's how you apply what you already know about yourself.

You will know that there are no more excuses, there is no reason to wait for timing, there will be no more training. We are uniquely brilliant from birth. That's the part I want you to embrace — your inherent brilliance you were born with years ago. You just need to learn how to identify your Purpose and your inner spark, then get about showing and sharing your gift to the world.

How To Use This Book

Materials List

Here are some items you might find handy for your journey through this book. If you have others to recommend, add them here, share on the Facebook Group and/or send a message to TheSpark.love

☐ Pen or Pencil.

☐ Optional Creative Supplies. Colored pencils and gel pens are recommended for use in the book. To use other creative supplies, download the coloring pages from theSpark.love and print on heavy paper for more creative play options.

☐ Sharpener

☐ Great Music. Bach Adagios, Jazz or whatever will put you in creative space.

☐ Headset for listening to the podcast.

☐ Podcast app for your phone so you can automatically download when you are connected to internet then listen anytime anyplace!

☐ Page markers or flags for marking your current place and other important places in this book.

☐ Quiet Space.

☐ Walking Shoes.

☐ Imagination.

☐ Willingness to Play.

☐ _____

☐ _____

☐ _____

☐ _____

☐ _____

☐ _____

☐ _____

☐ _____

☐ _____

How To Use This Book

Energy of the Day

In many traditions and cultures, the days of the week carry a unique energy, its own vibration. Just as an example I'll use the Greek names although all the cultures tap into similar energy. The Greeks originally named the days after the sun, the moon and planets which in turn were named from Greek Gods (and goddesses) which carry a unique energy.

Using the chart below, find the day of the week you are starting your Purpose Journey. Starting with Week One – Day One (and each day thereafter), capture the energy of the day by transferring the information from this chart and then writing, drawing, coloring, and commenting on the energy of the day.

Day of the Week	Energy of the Day	Color	Galactic Body	Greek Gods
Sunday	Gratitude, Success, Fame	Gold, Yellow	Sun	Helios
Monday	Emotional, Courage	Silver, White, Blue	Moon	Selene
Tuesday	Breakthrough, Courage	Red, Black, Orange	Mars	Aries
Wednesday	Change, Creativity	Purple, Orange	Mercury	Hermes
Thursday	Expansion, Abundance	Blue, Purple, Green	Jupiter	Zeus
Friday	Love, Friendship	Pink, Aqua	Venus	Aphrodite
Saturday	Grounded, Wisdom	Black, Purple	Saturn	Cronus

Other Considerations for the Energy of the Day
We are beings made up the elements: earth, air, fire, and water.
We are affected by the elements surrounding us. Notice these in your life:

Do you live by the ocean, desert, forest, grassland, or mountains? Do you live in a city, removed from natural variation? Do you feel differently when you go to another location that has an abundance of an element you're not used to having in your daily life?

The weather influences our energy and mood every day. Around the world, weather extremes are occurring more frequently; people are noticing how their life is affected by that weather. The moon, with its tidal pull, influences our energy, focus, and rhythm. Tracking the stages of the moon may offer insight to the fluctuations of your daily experiences.

Because you're starting this 28-day journey on your own schedule in the time and place where you are located, we'll offer no reference of a start date here for you such as Monday, Tuesday and so on. Each daily page has spaces where you can capture your location, the weather, and the stage of the moon. At the end of each week and at the end of the 28-day journey, review how the Energy of the Day was expressed in your life.

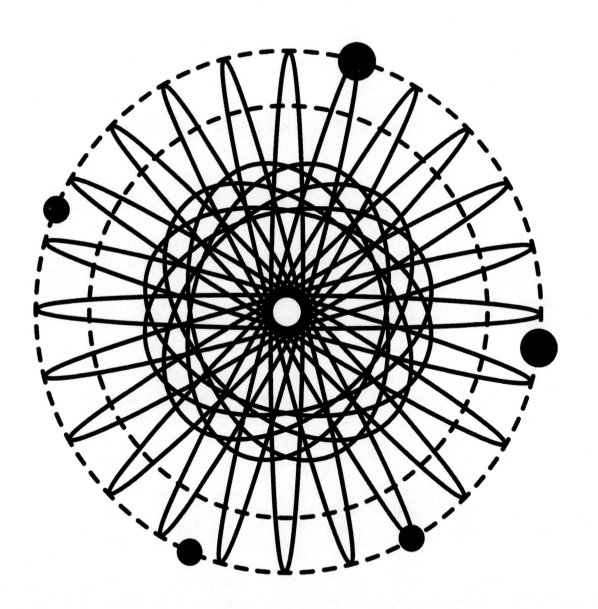

PURPOSE

You aren't confused about who you are. Really. Believe me—you aren't. You know your Purpose and understand your brilliance. You can tap into that place inside yourself where your intuition, your feelings, your Spark reside and know the authentic you. If you choose to stay in the energy of your brilliance every day, you would be swinging in the spotlight, and everyone else could see who you really are. You'd be totally authentically you, without confusion.

Granted, it may seem like you don't know your next step. Perhaps you are waiting for the thunderbolt of God-given-clarity paired with intuition as well as guidance to rain upon on your crown chakra before you make a step in any direction. Sorry. It's just not happening.

I'm here to confirm your deepest fear: you already know it all, and the lightning bolt isn't coming. Who you are, what you are here to do, and even how to get it done: it is all within you. Your thinking isn't confused at all.

In my many years of working with clients, I've never actually had one who was truly confused. Sometimes it has taken longer to get to the truth, due to the haze of confusion: however, it is always inside. These days, when I speak to someone for thirty minutes, as I ask a few questions, they start answering with full, truthful clarity. Though they may speak with resignation, it is from the heart, often with deep sighs as if they remember dreams long past that were put away on a shelf for later.

I get it. You're scared. Battered, bruised, and shell shocked, you've tried to step up to live your Purpose only to feel like you've been to battle. You've stepped off the cliff with confidence, and the net didn't appear. You moved forward with good faith and gotten ahead, yet not received that most radiant feeling when you know you are totally on track, guided, internally safe, and directed. It hasn't been easy. There have been deaths, trauma, losses, and well, just life.

It's also been fun. You've had a lot of successes: babies, promotions, and dancing at rock concerts. You've lived a life full of love and play along with sorrow and loss. Now every experience swirls together, caught up in resilience and tenacity, causing all sorts of confused thoughts in your head while simultaneously covering your blessed soul with fairy dust that has magically enslaved you from speaking your truth... Even to yourself.

Take this as your marching order: I'm hereby giving you permission to focus in order to connect with who you are right now in this time and place. Use this book with the intention that you'll get exactly what you need in order to accept all of who you are.

PURPOSE

Then you'll be able to take actions from the be-ing ness place, not the wondering or searching place, guilt-free.

In our turbulent world, we need focus, clarity, and strong intentional, aligned actions. Focus now so you can sort through the haze and clearly see who you are meant to be. After you see yourself for your true self, intention can carry you a long way. It's scary to admit it to ourselves, to realize we have these dreams and goals, and then we feel sad and inadequate for not following through— or worse, disappointed in ourselves. There are the emotions, too, especially the big one that shall not be named: SHAME.

We feel the shame of not doing what we said. We experience a deep longing to make a difference, to live on Purpose, with Purpose, and to have lives with meaning. It's wanting and knowing, but not following through that creates a deep shame.

On and on it goes. Examples of wanting to heal, help, speak, write, laugh, love all appear in ways to achieve our highest goals: We want to speak on big stages, and have dreams of inspiring millions, and desires to teach first grade. *Then* all the life distractions counter our hopeful thoughts with worries of paying the bills or getting the nit-picky things done.

Things in life drive us to forget that Purpose isn't doing; it's be-ing. That Purpose can be lived with or without your JOB, your career.

We feel we aren't living the dream life and then we pretend its confusion. Subsequently, we readily acknowledge as we laugh over coffee with friends, "Oh, I'm not sure what I want to do when I grow up." Really, it's just fear disguised as misguided modesty.

After all, we procrastinate, wash dishes, clean closets. These tasks are important because as we clean the clutter in our minds in similar fashion, it paves the way for clarity to see our Purpose. Yet somehow when we glimpse our clarity, we don't accept it, defaulting into labeling it procrastination, using it as a device to linger in make-believe confusion until something pushes us until we can't ignore it any longer.

When that happens, we hit bottom. It might come from an outside influence like a death of a loved one or (in my case) losing a successful business and all the benefits that came with it. These outside things (which could also be filing for divorce or quitting a job), as well as the items creating an internal chaos, force us to reconnect with who we are.

PURPOSE

We might go down fast, or we might see it approaching like an oncoming train without the ability to do a thing about it. We might even ask the Universe, "Help me find a way out of this situation," or "God, give me clarity," but still gob-smacked when the situation falls apart.

And still, the clarity will come, taking a day or months or years to resurface. But the bottom line is that we will have the clarity of our Purpose, and we can no longer pretend.

People always know what they really want, and even more specifically they usually know exactly what to do next to get there. What they lack is courage, and perhaps the brilliance of knowing, really knowing at their core who they are. They get distracted by other external circumstances, such as timing, preparation, luck, contacts, natural rhythms of life (like marriage, families, and illness/death) that take all of our energy for a while. When we wake, five or 20 years have passed, and we think: *What just happened?!*

We know we have something inside that needs to be expressed, but we settle for less because we don't want to see our true selves. If we did, it might cause radical change, or shift a small change, or inspire contemplation about our lives. It might cause us to connect with the Spark inside that keeps us curious about life. That could start a creative binge of dancing, traveling, camping in the wilderness, taking a six-week canoe trip, or just writing a little bit every day while we raise our families.

Let's look at it this way. You have a big beautiful silver bowl that's been sitting on the back shelf for ten years. It just needs a little hard work to clean it up and make it shine again so we can see its luminescence.

It wasn't that the shine was gone; it's just been covered.

Covered up with life.

Life is messy. People get sick, our beloved pets die. We suffer loss, and with each loss, we internalize it as a setback, something we've done wrong or that we didn't do at all. If we've experienced abuse or trauma, the covering of our brilliance is even more impactful with a full blanket that provides a cover of protection. I understand. I feel for you. But I want to see you shine.

It's time for a little spit and polish. Clean up the dust, put away the blanket, and allow the light inside to shine deeply. You can do this.

PURPOSE

I've also been there. Not in the same way as you because we all have different journeys. Part of my journey has included a wonderful family, business success, a home I adore, and a mostly happy marriage (it's 36 years, it can't be all roses). I've lived through personal and family illness. I've had an epic business failure, lived through home fire scares, hurricane winds, torrential floods, and massive hail. (We joke in our neighborhood that the locusts are coming). However, I have found something inside that keeps my light bright (at least most days) and I've learned that my life is bigger than just my immediate circumstance. We have things to do, people to help. We are still on Earth for a reason: BE-ing.

I feel the calling, hear the stirring. I rise, put on my shoes, and get to work doing my best. Every day, doing my best. It's about getting to "doing" and what we came here to do. But do-ing it from your place of be-ing.

It's complicated. It's tricky, and a little stress can push you over the edge where you are in only be-ing or only do-ing. We need them both to be balanced, helping each other. They function as mirrors for yourself. So yes, go DO, but only after you know how to BE.

You have to be brave to see your gifts and understand your Purpose. As you identify them, you'll find the more you should share and give back. It evokes into being called upon to give and share in a bigger way. You must see yourself first. Believe in yourself. Know yourself. Be brave.

Some people like to use a butterfly analogy that we're growing out of a cocoon into something more beautiful. Other people are reminded of an allegorical oyster hiding a pearl, where the shell must be cracked open to allow the beauty to breathe and be seen.

I love both images; however, they imply that you must evolve, change, and turn into something else for you to have a big transformation.

That's just not true.

You already are the transformation.

You already are the big beautiful butterfly that just needs to fly, the brilliant pearl breathing and glowing. Rather than having to emerge or change, let's just work on finding the shiny bit and allowing more of that to come through.

PURPOSE

I don't think you need to change, emerge, or grow to accept your brilliance. You need to dig deep and excavate for it. It's different for each of us. For some of us it's right there on the surface, and we are just waiting for permission to open up to ourselves so that we may see, acknowledge, and embrace who we are. If this is you, I invite you to step into your bright shiny self, be brave, and do what you came here to do. That's it. Now go do it.

No reason to even read the rest of this book.

For many of us, though, we are yearning to uncover those bits that have been buried. Sometimes we can't even find a shiny bit anymore because there's so much piled on top of it.

The layers of dirt and grime (tarnish?) may be abuse or trauma, but they can also just simply be years of living your life, raising children, going to work, and paying your light bill. In the process of all of this, you stepped back a little, which caused your light to dim. For those people, there's tons of hope; you just need to accept the past so as to integrate and move forward. If you need more support than this book gives you, I encourage you to seek out trauma specialists and get the help you desire. It is possible to heal from deep intense wounding. By spending a little time together, we will uncover that part inside of you that knows exactly how you are meant to be authentic in the world.

Authenticity emerges as your voice emerges as you practice being exactly who you are meant to be. You must be brave. This is a journey about trusting yourself first, counter to what we've been taught from day one.

We are shushed when we are hungry or tired, told to be quiet when we are crying. We've been told to share even when we don't want to share; we have to color a certain way, hold a pen "the correct way." We've all had big fat red X's through our writing at school, and told we are wrong for thinking or feeling a certain way. As we get into the teenage years with hormones, we second guess ourselves. People tell us to keep our emotions and hormones under control (as though there is something wrong with us). Then we are expected to have pursued one true calling, which we are supposed to know before we turn 20, and devote our lives to it?!

No wonder we cover ourselves with doubt, no longer trust our inner selves. The pattern is set to look to others to tell us how to feel, to get validation when we share. We post on social media and get our worth from Likes and Comments. Instead, we should *experience* life to understand our worth. Hike ten miles in an afternoon. Kayak around the lake every day for a year. Write a paragraph at two in the morning. Listen to yourself and acknowledge what emerges.

PURPOSE

It's similar to the first moment when you say I love you to a potential lover. You hope the words are returned because you are so very vulnerable with your truth that you believe you might not survive if it's not returned. The truth is that if you share I love you, it is your feeling in the moment, your truth; it shouldn't matter what others think or feel or how they respond.

In a less abstract example, if you eat a juicy apple, you can say, "Yummm, I love this." If someone responds, "Ugh, I don't like apples," it doesn't take away from your experience of the freshness of the fruit, and you don't stop loving the apple. When we allow ourselves to go deeper with our expression, we become more vulnerable; Often we accept other people's feedback as our truth rather than checking in and asking what it is that we know about ourselves.

Imagine, sharing something and it's met with silence. We start second guessing. Was I wrong to say it? Have I shared too much? Won't he like me anymore? Did I overstep?

It was your truth! Why are we so afraid to share our truth?

We become embarrassed with silence or ridicule, and it becomes our excuse to stop being truth-tellers to ourselves. We stop being brave.

We return to listening to others, taking their truth as ours. We no longer know what our own truth is. We are taught to reach, strive, and work through our baggage. Let go of issues. Understand your triggers, embrace your flaws, and focus on polishing yourself. We need you, in your full glory. Now.

Yep, I know you don't have to chase your Purpose, don't have to go somewhere to find it, don't have to go seeking how to live it. It's already within you, alive and well, bursting to be seen at the highest levels. After searching for my Purpose for years while chasing the dream and looking for answers (physics, readings, coaching, assessments, books; you name it, I did it), one day I realized I was happy. I was already living my Purpose and feeling fulfilled.

Fulfilled became my key word, so I would use it to evaluate if I felt like I was doing what I came here to do. As someone who knows that we teach what we need to learn, I'd already been doing 'Purpose' coaching (and business consulting) for ten years before I came to the realization I was already living my Purpose. I'd read every book, followed masters on the subject, studied various spiritual teachings; still, I hadn't been happy. I was the common denominator. Everything kept pointing back to me. Look inside. The answers are within. Huh. I didn't know how to look inside.

PURPOSE

As balanced and 'healed' as I might have claimed to be, I couldn't see my authenticity to understand what would make me 'visible' to my clients, my tribe, my family, but most importantly to myself.

When living your Purpose, you will be in action and yet it won't feel like. It won't feel like you are doing anything. You will simply *Be*. Your Purpose is not a job, activity, or a role. Many people feel lost when they lose a job, a role, or no longer engage in an activity they once loved. While you may feel fulfillment when engaging in one of these, this is not your Purpose. These are all containers in which you can manifest your Purpose, but these containers are not your Purpose (yes, it's a lower case because it's not your higher capital letter Purpose).

Focusing on "what you do for a living" is such a western (especially American) thematic way of looking at the world. You need to ignore what they are saying on the outside and listen to what you are hearing on the inside.

When you are almost "there" to having that clarity, it could feel like it's the place where you get the most stuck. I know, I've built several million-dollar businesses, lost partners, overcome illness, nursed others back to health, traveled the world, and fostered ten children—but you know what stops me dead in my tracks? It's the fear that I'll go to my grave with my dreams still inside me, the fear that I didn't do what I was meant to do.

It's so much easier to take concrete actions, get my butt in gear, purchase a plane ticket, or even waste hours on Facebook rather than lean in to be deeply honest about my dreams. Some may say this is all procrastination, but part of procrastination is waiting until the right time (not a late time) to accomplish something—accomplishing the identity of your Purpose is worth not procrastinating! (Watch my TEDx talk on this subject, where I get really into it). You need to get to your state of be-ing so you can feel and intuitively understand your own timing. Then, when you are procrastinating you'll know it's true, and when you are waiting, incubating, watching, learning, you'll understand that is part of your process.

Your Purpose is not a thing; it is a verb. When living your Purpose, you will not be in action. You will simply Be.

Let's look at it a different way. Honor your mind with all the thinking it can do. Give it undivided attention in this process. Wrap your brain around this. Think a lot. Wonder what your Purpose is. Take a lot of quizzes, ask other people. Write yourself notes, read books and use that mind until it's so confused and full that you think you have nothing left to do but drop to your knees in wonder. It's then that asking and finally surrendering allows your true nature to reveal itself to you.

PURPOSE

Your Life is your Purpose. You can't help but live your Purpose. You don't need to chase it, understand it, or strive for it. You <u>are</u> it. You are already living your Purpose. It's not outside of you; all the books and assessments in the world won't help you get it. (I know, I've tried.) You have a Purpose because you are here, alive in this world.

Remember in the largest broadest sense our Purpose is to learn to love bigger, bolder, stronger. We learn to love ourselves, our neighbors, and humanity. I suspect you want all that plus more. You want to know exactly how to live your Purpose, express who you are in a way that is in alignment with who you are being.

Ok. Now Go. Live and Be.

Use the following pages to re-align with what you already know deep inside of you.

PURPOSE Sample Pages

Here, and on the following pages, you will find a variety of sample pages which you can use for your own inspiration. As you can see there is no wrong or right way to do these, just allow your own eclectic creativity to come through!

You will also find more pages on the TheSpark.love website and we encourage you to upload your own pages to the Facebook group as inspiration for others.

SPARK Wheel

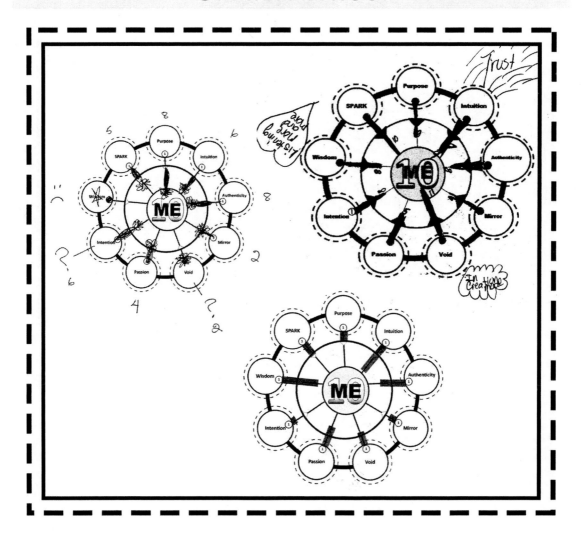

15

PURPOSE Sample Pages

Elemental Mind Map

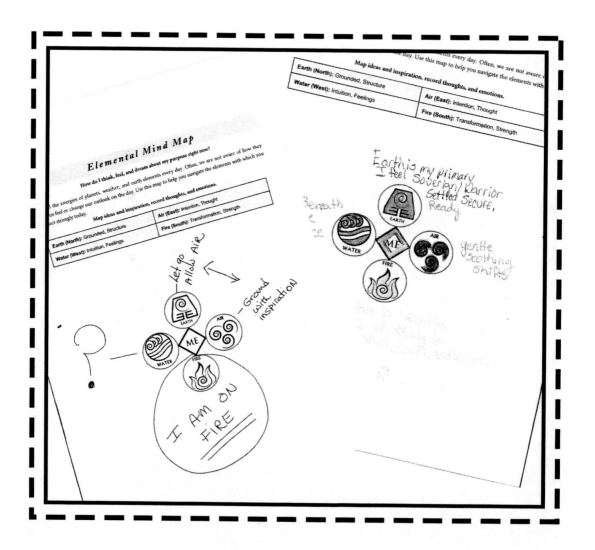

PURPOSE Sample Pages

Purpose Avatar

PURPOSE
The 28-Day Focus:

To ground and root my purpose

Message from Michelle: If you are alive you are living your purpose. You can't help but live it. You don't have to chase it, dream about it or look for it. Simply be, and allow more of yourself to shine and that is your purpose. Think of it this way:

Your purpose is how you express yourself
and your love out into the world. Naturally.

If you can get out of your head, always thinking about me me me and move into a place helping, serving, and radically truthful loving, then you will connect strongly with your purpose - even if you never know 'exactly' what it is, you will feel in purpose.

Imagine this: I feel on Purpose. I know I am serving and helping and contributing in some way just by being alive. Sometimes this feels like a color, or a feeling, or a knowing. Ground the feeling and the knowing as best you can. Give your purpose a shape, color, sound, and smell. Is it something you access outside of yourself when you need to? Can you relate to it if you give it another name?
Draw your Purpose icon or avatar:

Affirmation:
I am aware of the Energy of the Day
and how it affects me.

PURPOSE Sample Pages

Mind Clutter

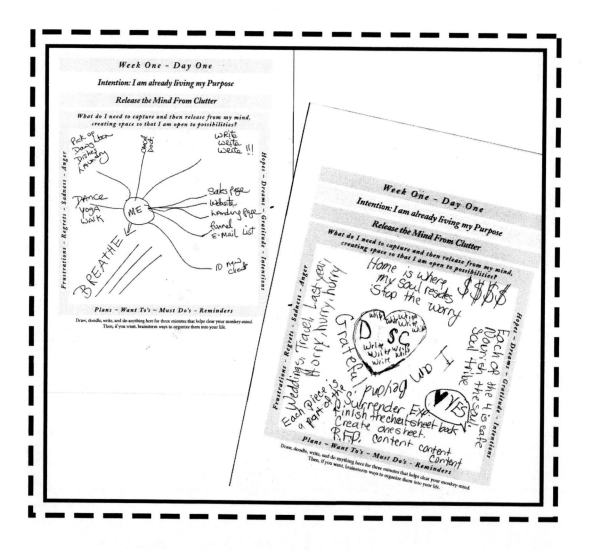

PURPOSE Sample Pages

Energy of the Day

SPARK Assessment Questions

Inner Contemplations

- **Purpose:**

   Am I grounded and rooted in what I am here to do and how I give back to society and the planet? How do I express my love out into the world?

- **Intuition:**

   Do I hear the whispers in my ear and inside my body? Do I recognize it as my intuition?

- **Authenticity:**

   Am I able to see myself for who I truly am? Do I live and speak my truth?

Outer Reflections

- **Mirror:**

   When I look out at the world do I see how my life is reflected back to me? Am I open to the life lessons?

- **Void:**

   Am I open to the greatest mysteries in life? Am I able to accept the roller coaster of what comes?

- **Passion:**

   Do I have hobbies, interests, curiosities about the world? Am I allowing my passion, (charisma) to attract like minds and souls to me?

Living and Be-ing

- **Intention:**

   What is the vision for my life and legacy? Do I have clear intentions while staying open to the journey?

- **Wisdom:**

   Do I feel wise? Do I honor the natural cycles in my life?

- **SPARK:**

   Overall, how is the inner flame? Feeling alive and adventurous?

SPARK Assessment

Now that you know a bit about each aspect of the SPARK series, self-evaluate where you are today on a scale of one to ten using the *inner ME* as a perfect ten and the outer bubbles as one (the starting point). Use colored stars, different line styles, map a grid, or draw thought bubbles in order to track your progress and movement throughout the month.

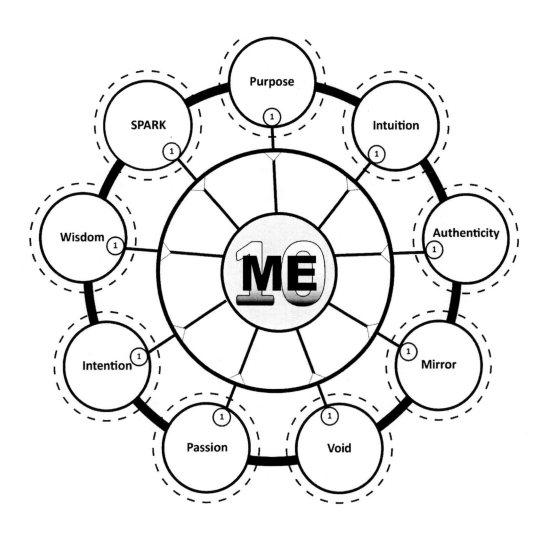

Elemental Mind Map

We feel the energies of planets, weather, and earth elements every day. Often, we are not aware of how they make us feel or change our outlook on the day. Use this map to help you navigate the elements which you connect with strongly today. Know, that at this moment in time, this is what's true and also know that it may change. If you like, come back and revisit this mind map over the next 28 days.

Map ideas and inspiration, record thoughts, and emotions.

Earth (North): Grounded, Structure   **Air (East):** Intention, Thought

Water (West): Intuition, Feelings   **Fire (South):** Transformation, Strength

The Energy of Purpose

There are hundreds of tools, maps, blueprints, and systems for Purpose. Four of my favorites are chosen below to help you start this journey (including one I developed and use with my clients), but learning (or remembering) Purpose can't be found by searching outward. **It's already inside.**

On the following pages, you'll find some very abbreviated methods to help identify your Energy of Purpose. These items are not the 'be all and end all' of getting anchored in Purpose, but they will confirm existing ideas as well as offer a new energy to ponder. Every day of this 28-day journey, you'll explore the Energy of the Day and observe its influence on your life. For now, let's explore the Energy of Purpose...

The Energy of the Life Path Number

By using the universal language of numbers, information about you and the world is revealed through the relationship and personalities attributed to each number. For some calculations, the letters of the alphabet have specific numerical equivalents important to you, too.

Discover your Life Path number, which is based on your birthdate. This is the blueprint number for your life ; it influences the opportunities and challenges you will encounter. Your Life Path number gives you clues to your Purpose.

➔ **Please feel free to ignore this page if it's too much math!**

How to Calculate Your Life Path Number

First reduce each unit of your birth date (two-digit month/two-digit day/four-digit year) to a single-digit number, which is also called a Significant (aka Master) number.

In order to do this, add each of the digits (or Master numbers) together and until you reduce the total to a single digit, the Significant number.

For example, if your birthday is November 16, 1960 you would add your numbers this way:

- November is the 11th month of the year. Eleven reduces to 2 (1 + 1 = 2).
- The day of birth is 16. (1 + 6 = 7).
- The year of birth is 1960. (1 + 9 + 6 + 0 = 16, then 1 + 6 = 7).
- Now add the resulting single-digit numbers: 2 + 7 + 7 = 16, 1 + 6 = 7.
- The Life Path number in this case is 7.
- Using the chart to the right, the energy of 7 is Investigation and Evaluation.

1	Leader, Independent
2	Peacemaker, Fixer
3	Creator, Communicator
4	Planner, Builder
5	Adventurous, Curious
6	Nurturer, Truth
7	Investigation, Evaluation
8	Lead, Govern
9	Humanitarian, Compassion
Other Significant Numbers:	
11	Master Teacher, Enlightener
22	Creates & Builds Global Projects
33	Significant Spiritual Leader

```
MONTH:              =
DAY:                =
YEAR:               =
MONTH + DAY + YEAR  = LIFE PATH NUMBER

_____  +  _____  +  _____  =  _____
```

The Energy of the Sun Sign

Your Sun Sign is a representation of the location of the Sun relative to your location at the exact moment of your birth. Symbolically, it is associated with your vitality, creativity, and personality. It is the initial outward expression of your life and many believe it relates directly to your Purpose.

ARIES - The Ram
(March 21 – April 19)
Pioneer, Trailblazer

LEO: The Lion
(July 23-Aug 22)
Expression, Emotional

SAGITTARIUS: The Archer
(Nov 22-Dec 21)
Dreamer, Fearless

TAURUS - The Bull
(Apr 20-May 20)
Security, Cooperation

VIRGO: The Virgin
(Aug 23-Sep 22)
Service, Wellbeing

CAPRICORN: The Goat
(Dec 22-Jan 19)
Structure, Grounded

GEMINI - The Twins
(May 21-Jun 20)
Communication, Authenticity

LIBRA: The Scales
(Sep 23-Oct 22)
Balance, Harmony

AQUARIUS: The Water Bearer
(Jan 20-Feb 18)
Innovation, Social Justice

CANCER - The Crab
(June 21-July 22)
Family, Feelings

SCORPIO: The Scorpion
(Oct 23-Nov 21)
Intensity, Magnetic

PISCES: The Fish
(Feb 19-Mar 20)
Healer, Artistic

To learn more about astrology and how it relates to your Purpose and your SPARK, visit here: http://theSpark.love/astro

The Energy of Marketing Archetypes

Archetypes are an ancient system that was expanded by Jung (as well as many others); it is a pattern and has been brought into personal development. Using Jung's work as a base, I developed them a system of Marketing Archetypes to help you relate to your working life. Archetypes give us a focus — a place to understand when we are working from our strengths or when we are stressed to the point of working from our weaknesses. These systems are looking for threads, as in energies and consistencies that go through your life.

Most people fall into one or two Marketing Archetypes categories. You may be more than one of these, but one might be more prominent or more joyful for you than others: Star, Mystic, Professor, Creator, Mechanic, Caregiver, Politician.

I bet you find yourself gravitating to one type over another. For instance, I'd rather see myself as a Creator than a Caregiver. However, I'm also a caregiver and love when I'm with my family in that role. I embrace it, but it's not my first choice as I know that I wouldn't go out of my way to care for others that I don't know.

Here's where it gets convoluted and twisted for us. We expect that our Purpose is the way we make our living. Your inner dialogue says, "I want to make a living as an artist, which is a creator type, but if I'm a caregiver, I should go to nursing school." (You can insert your own example here.)

Ack! What pressure we put on ourselves. We shout inside, "I'm not making my living doing what I'm supposed to be doing."

We scurry in our brain trying to figure it all out, and beat ourselves up when we aren't doing it right. No NO NO! I'll say it again and reassure you that you are already living your Purpose. Even when you go about your day, you are probably holding your Energy of Purpose in every activity. So, you need to recognize and embrace the many ways we can identify with Purpose. Archetypes are one way.

On the next page, read through each Marketing Archetype description and identify the Archetype(s) that resonate for you and how they relate to Purpose in your life.

The Energy of Marketing Archetypes

STAR – Visionary, Masses, Destination

In Balance: Warm in person, optimistic, big visions, connect with the masses, believes big dreams conquer the world

Out of Balance: Egotistical, blow off people, doesn't listen well

MYSTIC – Visionary, 1 – 1, Journey

In Balance: Highly intuitive, very spiritual, often off in other realms, in touch with emotions, teach and model big concepts

Out of Balance: Not well-rounded, doesn't care about results, not enough planning, too trusting in the Universe, picks up emotions and keeps them

PROFESSOR – Practical, Masses, Journey

In Balance: Dig deep, love of learning, thoughtful, wise, practical and intelligent

Out of Balance: Gets caught up in explaining, talks too much or too long, focuses on the destination not the journey

CREATOR – Visionary, Masses, Journey

In Balance: Short term focus with big creative bursts, easily creates products, often visual, one strong sensory perception outweighs the others

Out of Balance: Tries to do too much, not finishing projects or products, needs to focus and be told what to do

MECHANIC – Practical, Small Groups, Destination

In Balance: Systems, demonstrations, templates, accountability, wants to see big picture

Out of Balance: Too much detail on paper, caught up in the system instead of results

CAREGIVER – Practical, 1 – 1, Journey

In Balance: Selfless service, gives from love, healing energy, cares deeply, connects intimately and quickly, no expectations

Out of Balance: Becomes bossy mothers, gives too much of self with nothing left, holds martyr energy, feels unappreciated

POLITICIAN – Visionary, Masses, Destination

In Balance: Brings people together, great networkers and connectors, knows people and remembers names and faces, concerned with outcome

Out of Balance: Uses others to get to the top, little regard for process, the end justifies the means

The Energy of Your Human Design

Get your free Human Design chart at
http://theSpark.love/HD

This is the Human Design Mandala.
Human Design is the synthesis of these systems:
- IChing
- Western and Eastern Astrology
- Chakras
- Kabbalah
- Quantum Physics

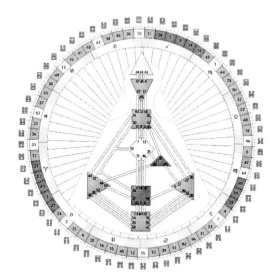

There are four Human Design Types:

Manifestor
Life Purpose: Leading change by sharing new ideas, pushing people beyond their comfort level and empowering others to do things in new ways, get things started
Role: Initiate action from ideas and from their own inner creative flow

Generator / Manifesting Generator
Life Purpose: Doing things over and over again in various ways and forms to learn and as well as achieve mastery, focused on finding the shortest path, striving to become masterful at embodying the energy of creativity, effectively being the builders of the world.
Role: To find the right work and the right partner in life (and finding the fastest way).

Projector
The Life Purpose: Managing and guiding others, having innate wisdom about what others need, applying their instinctive impulse about using their wisdom to make the world a better place and alleviate people's pain and suffering.
Role: To manage, guide and direct the energies of others.

Reflector
Life Purpose: Reflecting the health of communities back to others via impersonal experience, learning the truth of "this isn't me" again and again, understanding the greatest potential is complete transparency.
Role: Reflecting the health and alignment of the people around them.

The Energy of My Purpose

_____   My Life Path Number

My Life Path Traits:

_____   My Sun Sign

What I Need to Remember About My Sun Sign:

_____   My Marketing Archetype

What I Need to Remember About My Marketing Archetype:

_____   My Human Design Type

What I Need to Remember About My Human Design Type:

If you have experience with any other systems (such as Enneagram, DISC, Myers Briggs, Vedic Astrology) record them here:

♥ _____

♥ _____

♥ _____

♥ _____

♥ _____

PURPOSE
The 28-Day Focus:

To ground and root my Purpose

If you are alive you are living your Purpose. You can't help but live it. You don't have to chase it, dream about it or look for it. Simply be, and allow more of yourself to shine and that is your Purpose. Think of it this way:

**Your Purpose is how you express yourself
and your love out into the world. Naturally.**

If you can get out of your head, always thinking about me me me and move into a place helping, serving, and radically truthful loving, then you will connect strongly with your Purpose - even if you never know 'exactly' what it is, you will feel in Purpose.

Imagine this: I feel on Purpose. I know I am serving and helping and contributing in some way just by being alive. Sometimes this feels like a color, or a feeling, or a knowing. Ground the feeling and the knowing as best you can. Give your Purpose a shape, color, sound, and smell. Is it something you access outside of yourself when you need to? Can you relate to it if you give it another name?
Draw your Purpose icon or avatar:

Affirmation:
I am aware of the Energy of the Day and how it affects me.

Suggested Tool for the Month:
Purpose Alignment Oil

30

PURPOSE
The 28-Day Focus:

Activity Focus - Breathe

Go to theSpark.love to find an audio guided meditation for this exercise.

Every day, Michelle invites you to embrace these actions:

1. As soon as you get out of bed, put both feet on the floor and sink deep into the soles of your feet.
2. Imagine growing roots and grounding yourself into the center of the earth.
3. Feel yourself awake.
4. Reach your arms to the heavens.
5. Allow your spine to straighten, but relax your shoulders.
6. Keep your feet growing roots.
7. Imagine connecting with both heaven and earth with your body the vehicle connecting them.
8. Allow the energy to bounce upwards, through your spine and out the top of your head into the channel that extends up into the heavens for divine inspiration.

Support Yourself All Day:
- Take three deep breaths in a cycle periodically throughout the day.
- Acknowledge to yourself, "I am alive."
- Breathe into your feet as you go about your day to ground myself.
- Breathe into your crown and to the heavens in order to encourage inspiration.

Week One

To help clear your mind and launch your week,
color, draw, doodle, and play with this weekly mandala...

I am already living my Purpose

Week One

Color and decorate your weekly intention to ground it. You might want to add stickers or collage this page. If you wish, you can create a vision board around this intention. (As a reminder, a vision board is a visual prompt to help you focus on a specific goal or intention. You can use images that represent whatever this means to you.)

Internalize the intention by speaking it out loud and to yourself. Include the intention in your daily meditation, walk, or other practice. Ponder it through out the week.

This is the Weekly Intention:

I am already living my Purpose

Everything you do relates to and supports this intention.
It is Big Picture Wisdom.
Be attentive to how it appears in your life this week.

Week One

This is what the weekly intention looks like to you.
Draw, doodle, write, paste pictures – Create your vision of the weekly intention.

My Daily Action Plan for the Week

- Start my day by breathing and grounding
- Remember and reflect upon the weekly intention
- Color, draw, doodle the daily mandala
- Do the Daily Mind Clearing
- Explore the Energy of the Day
- Review the Daily Contemplation, and capture how it manifest for me
- Allow time in my day to reflect and deepen my experience
- Listen to the SPARK Podcast to inspire and ground this weekly intention

Week One

What Activities Support You?

Envision the next seven days.
What activities support and ground you as you move through the day?
What keeps you balanced, relieves stress and stimulates your creative juices?
Identify those activities on this list and add your own. If you like, post them in the Facebook group so everyone can share in the limitless supportive possibilities. Also capture those you would like to try someday.

This is not a commandment or a 'have-to must-do." It's an opportunity to explore self-care in whatever form that it works for you. We'll ask you every day to note what you did or what you plan to do. If it feels like too much pressure – skip it. Come back to it some other time when it feels right.

✓ Doing It   ● On the List Someday

- O Walk in Nature
- O Meditate / Be Still
- O Do Yoga or Stretch
- O Write or Journal
- O Nap or Sleep
- O Read a Book
- O Get a Massage or
- O Other Self Care
- O Cook & Eat a Healthy Meal
- O Go to the Gym
- O Run or Jog
- O Bike, Ski or Other Active Solo Sport
- O Play a Team Sport
- O Do Tai Chi or Qigong
- O Take Time for Your Hobby
- O Learn Something New

- O Play with Kids / Family
- O Devote Quality Time to Your Spouse
- O Connect With Friends
- O Connect With Pet(s)
- O Make Art / Be Creative
- O Organize or Clean Belongings
- O Sing or Make Music
- O Play an Instrument
- O Dance (Solo or with a Partner)
- O Get Wet (Swim, Paddle Board, Surf)
- O Take a Relaxing Bath

Week One

During the weekly podcast, I offer tips and ideas to move even more deeply into your Purpose. Some weeks there are guest experts; we discuss everything from creativity, authenticity, and building your life on Purpose. There are also experts who use different tools to discover Purpose. I invite you to doodle, dream, and take notes while you listen – or come back later (if you listen in the car or elsewhere). Then jot down your thoughts here:

Weekly Podcast

Week One

Weekly Podcast

Looking at your notes, what thoughts, ideas, and inspirations what do you want to capture from this week's SPARK: The Radically Authentic Life podcast?

☐ _____

☐ _____

☐ _____

☐ _____

☐ _____

☐ _____

Using these notes, what does it look like to you?
What ideas and thoughts of yours link to those from the podcast?
How are you inspired by what you heard?
Consider using thought bubbles to track the connections and flow.

Week One - Day One

Day of the Week: _____   *Today's Date:* _____

To help clear your mind and ground your day,
color, draw, doodle, and play with this daily mandala...

Briefly write about how you noticed Purpose was active in your life yesterday

Week One - Day One

Intention: I am already living my Purpose

Release the Mind From Clutter

What do I need to capture and then release from my mind, creating space so that I am open to possibilities?

Frustrations - Regrets - Sadness - Anger

Hopes – Dreams – Gratitude - Intentions

Plans – Want To's – Must Do's - Reminders

Draw, doodle, write, and do anything here for three minutes that helps clear your monkey-mind.
Then, if you want, brainstorm ways to organize them into your life.

Week One - Day One

The Energy of the Day

Today, pay attention to all of the different elements and influences around you (besides family, friends, work, etc.). After the 28 days of recording, you'll find you can predict your energy/moods and feelings, then use them to your benefit. (Some days more intuitive, some days more productive.)

See page 5 for the Energy of the Day reference chart.

Today's Galactic Body:

_____

What is the phase of the moon?

_____

What is the element of your location?
(Earth, Air, Fire, Water)

_____

What is the Energy of the Day today?

_____

What are today's colors?

_____

What is the weather today?
(Especially note extreme weather)

_____

How do you notice and respond to the Energy of the Day?
Draw, doodle, write, paste pictures/words.
Explore your way to express the Energy of the Day and perhaps your energy, too.

I chose this activity or activities to support my self-care today:

Week One - Day One

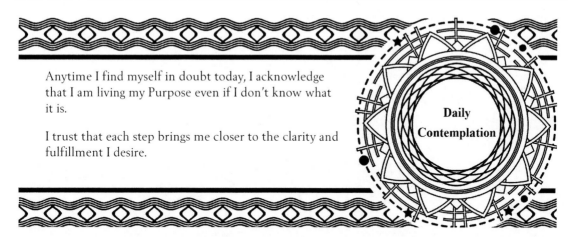

Anytime I find myself in doubt today, I acknowledge that I am living my Purpose even if I don't know what it is.

I trust that each step brings me closer to the clarity and fulfillment I desire.

Daily Contemplation

Color, draw, doodle, and write about the above Daily Contemplation. Speak it out loud and to yourself to help internalize it. Include it in your daily meditation, walk or other practice. Notice when situations and circumstances arise where you can apply the Daily Contemplation.

What the Daily Contemplation Looks Like to Me:

How will you implement or integrate the Daily Contemplation today?

Week One - Day Two

Day of the Week: _____   *Today's Date:* _____

To help clear your mind and ground your day,
color, draw, doodle, and play with this daily mandala...

Briefly write about how you noticed Purpose was active in your life yesterday

Week One - Day Two

Intention: I am already living my Purpose

Release the Mind From Clutter

*What do I need to capture and then release from my mind,
creating space so that I am open to possibilities?*

Frustrations - Regrets - Sadness - Anger

Hopes – Dreams – Gratitude - Intentions

Plans – Want To's – Must Do's - Reminders

Draw, doodle, write, and do anything here for three minutes that helps clear your monkey-mind.
Then, if you want, brainstorm ways to organize them into your life.

Week One - Day Two

The Energy of the Day

Today, pay attention to all of the different elements and influences around you (besides family, friends, work, etc.). After the 28 days of recording, you'll find you can predict your energy/ moods and feelings, then use them to your benefit. (Some days more intuitive, some days more productive.)

See page 5 for the Energy of the Day reference chart.

Today's Galactic Body:

_____

What is the phase of the moon?

_____

What is the element of your location?
(Earth, Air, Fire, Water)

_____

What is the Energy of the Day today?

_____

What are today's colors?

_____

What is the weather today?
(Especially note extreme weather)

_____

How do you notice and respond to the Energy of the Day?
Draw, doodle, write, paste pictures/words.
Explore your way to express the Energy of the Day and perhaps your energy, too.

I chose this activity or activities to support my self-care today:

Week One - Day Two

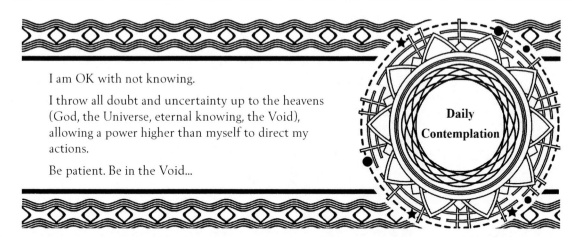

I am OK with not knowing.

I throw all doubt and uncertainty up to the heavens (God, the Universe, eternal knowing, the Void), allowing a power higher than myself to direct my actions.

Be patient. Be in the Void...

Daily Contemplation

Color, draw, doodle, and write about the above Daily Contemplation. Speak it out loud and to yourself to help internalize it. Include it in your daily meditation, walk or other practice. Notice when situations and circumstances arise where you can apply the Daily Contemplation.

What the Daily Contemplation Looks Like to Me:

How will you implement or integrate the Daily Contemplation today?

Week One - Day Three

Day of the Week: _____   *Today's Date:* _____

To help clear your mind and ground your day,
color, draw, doodle, and play with this daily mandala...

Briefly write about how you noticed Purpose was active in your life yesterday

Week One - Day Three

Intention: I am already living my Purpose

Release the Mind From Clutter

What do I need to capture and then release from my mind, creating space so that I am open to possibilities?

Frustrations - Regrets - Sadness - Anger

Hopes – Dreams – Gratitude - Intentions

Plans – Want To's – Must Do's - Reminders

Draw, doodle, write, and do anything here for three minutes that helps clear your monkey-mind. Then, if you want, brainstorm ways to organize them into your life.

Week One - Day Three

The Energy of the Day

Today, pay attention to all of the different elements and influences around you (besides family, friends, work, etc.). After the 28 days of recording, you'll find you can predict your energy/ moods and feelings, then use them to your benefit. (Some days more intuitive, some days more productive.)

See page 5 for the Energy of the Day reference chart.

Today's Galactic Body:

_____

What is the phase of the moon?

_____

What is the element of your location?
(Earth, Air, Fire, Water)

_____

What is the Energy of the Day today?

_____

What are today's colors?

_____

What is the weather today?
(Especially note extreme weather)

_____

How do you notice and respond to the Energy of the Day?
Draw, doodle, write, paste pictures/words.
Explore your way to express the Energy of the Day and perhaps your energy, too.

I chose this activity or activities to support my self-care today:

Week One - Day Three

What happens if I never know my Purpose?

Daily Contemplation

Color, draw, doodle, and write about the above Daily Contemplation. Speak it out loud and to yourself to help internalize it. Include it in your daily meditation, walk or other practice. Notice when situations and circumstances arise where you can apply the Daily Contemplation.

What the Daily Contemplation Looks Like to Me:

How will you implement or integrate the Daily Contemplation today?

Week One - Day Four

Day of the Week: _____   *Today's Date:* _____

To help clear your mind and ground your day,
color, draw, doodle, and play with this daily mandala...

Briefly write about how you noticed Purpose was active in your life yesterday

Week One - Day Four

Intention: I am already living my Purpose

Release the Mind From Clutter

What do I need to capture and then release from my mind, creating space so that I am open to possibilities?

Frustrations - Regrets - Sadness - Anger

Hopes – Dreams – Gratitude - Intentions

Plans – Want To's – Must Do's - Reminders

Draw, doodle, write, and do anything here for three minutes that helps clear your monkey-mind.
Then, if you want, brainstorm ways to organize them into your life.

Week One - Day Four

The Energy of the Day

Today, pay attention to all of the different elements and influences around you (besides family, friends, work, etc.). After the 28 days of recording, you'll find you can predict your energy/moods and feelings, then use them to your benefit. (Some days more intuitive, some days more productive.)

See page 5 for the Energy of the Day reference chart.

Today's Galactic Body:

_____

What is the phase of the moon?

_____

What is the element of your location?
(Earth, Air, Fire, Water)

_____

What is the Energy of the Day today?

_____

What are today's colors?

_____

What is the weather today?
(Especially note extreme weather)

_____

How do you notice and respond to the Energy of the Day?
Draw, doodle, write, paste pictures/words.
Explore your way to express the Energy of the Day and perhaps your energy, too.

I chose this activity or activities to support my self-care today:

Week One - Day Four

I look to my peers.

Who are the people I admire that are already living their Purpose?

Daily Contemplation

Color, draw, doodle, and write about the above Daily Contemplation. Speak it out loud and to yourself to help internalize it. Include it in your daily meditation, walk or other practice. Notice when situations and circumstances arise where you can apply the Daily Contemplation.

What the Daily Contemplation Looks Like to Me:

How will you implement or integrate the Daily Contemplation today?

Week One - Day Five

Day of the Week: _____   *Today's Date:* _____

To help clear your mind and ground your day,
color, draw, doodle, and play with this daily mandala...

Briefly write about how you noticed Purpose was active in your life yesterday

Week One - Day Five

Intention: I am already living my Purpose

Release the Mind From Clutter

What do I need to capture and then release from my mind, creating space so that I am open to possibilities?

Frustrations - Regrets - Sadness - Anger

Hopes – Dreams – Gratitude - Intentions

Plans – Want To's – Must Do's - Reminders

Draw, doodle, write, and do anything here for three minutes that helps clear your monkey-mind.
Then, if you want, brainstorm ways to organize them into your life.

Week One - Day Five

The Energy of the Day

Today, pay attention to all of the different elements and influences around you (besides family, friends, work, etc.). After the 28 days of recording, you'll find you can predict your energy/ moods and feelings, then use them to your benefit. (Some days more intuitive, some days more productive.)

See page 5 for the Energy of the Day reference chart.

Today's Galactic Body:

_____

What is the phase of the moon?

_____

What is the element of your location?
(Earth, Air, Fire, Water)

_____

What is the Energy of the Day today?

_____

What are today's colors?

_____

What is the weather today?
(Especially note extreme weather)

_____

How do you notice and respond to the Energy of the Day?
Draw, doodle, write, paste pictures/words.
Explore your way to express the Energy of the Day and perhaps your energy, too.

I chose this activity or activities to support my self-care today:

Week One - Day Five

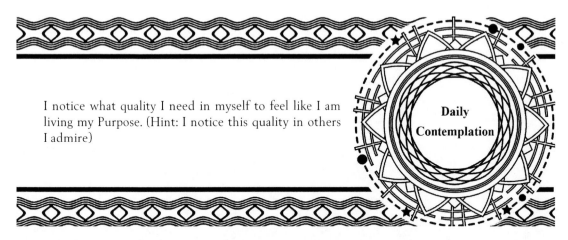

I notice what quality I need in myself to feel like I am living my Purpose. (Hint: I notice this quality in others I admire)

Daily Contemplation

Color, draw, doodle, and write about the above Daily Contemplation. Speak it out loud and to yourself to help internalize it. Include it in your daily meditation, walk or other practice. Notice when situations and circumstances arise where you can apply the Daily Contemplation.

What the Daily Contemplation Looks Like to Me:

How will you implement or integrate the Daily Contemplation today?

Week One - Day Six

Day of the Week: _____   *Today's Date:* _____

To help clear your mind and ground your day,
color, draw, doodle, and play with this daily mandala...

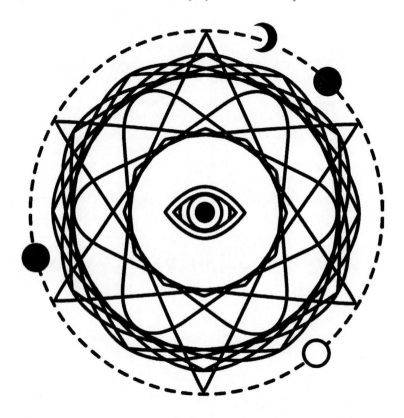

Briefly write about how you noticed Purpose was active in your life yesterday

Week One - Day Six

Intention: I am already living my Purpose

Release the Mind From Clutter

What do I need to capture and then release from my mind, creating space so that I am open to possibilities?

Frustrations - Regrets - Sadness - Anger

Hopes – Dreams – Gratitude - Intentions

Plans – Want To's – Must Do's - Reminders

Draw, doodle, write, and do anything here for three minutes that helps clear your monkey-mind. Then, if you want, brainstorm ways to organize them into your life.

Week One - Day Six

The Energy of the Day

Today, pay attention to all of the different elements and influences around you (besides family, friends, work, etc.). After the 28 days of recording, you'll find you can predict your energy/ moods and feelings, then use them to your benefit. (Some days more intuitive, some days more productive.)

See page 5 for the Energy of the Day reference chart.

Today's Galactic Body:

_____

What is the phase of the moon?

_____

What is the element of your location?
(Earth, Air, Fire, Water)

_____

What is the Energy of the Day today?

_____

What are today's colors?

_____

What is the weather today?
(Especially note extreme weather)

_____

How do you notice and respond to the Energy of the Day?
Draw, doodle, write, paste pictures/words.
Explore your way to express the Energy of the Day and perhaps your energy, too.

I chose this activity or activities to support my self-care today:

Week One - Day Six

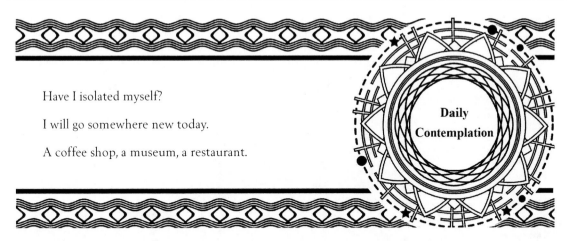

Have I isolated myself?

I will go somewhere new today.

A coffee shop, a museum, a restaurant.

Color, draw, doodle, and write about the above Daily Contemplation. Speak it out loud and to yourself to help internalize it. Include it in your daily meditation, walk or other practice. Notice when situations and circumstances arise where you can apply the Daily Contemplation.

What the Daily Contemplation Looks Like to Me:

How will you implement or integrate the Daily Contemplation today?

Week One - Day Seven

Day of the Week: _____   *Today's Date:* _____

To help clear your mind and ground your day,
color, draw, doodle, and play with this daily mandala...

Briefly write about how you noticed Purpose was active in your life yesterday

Week One - Day Seven

Intention: I am already living my Purpose

Release the Mind From Clutter

What do I need to capture and then release from my mind, creating space so that I am open to possibilities?

Frustrations - Regrets - Sadness - Anger

Hopes – Dreams – Gratitude - Intentions

Plans – Want To's – Must Do's - Reminders

Draw, doodle, write, and do anything here for three minutes that helps clear your monkey-mind. Then, if you want, brainstorm ways to organize them into your life.

Week One - Day Seven

The Energy of the Day

Today, pay attention to all of the different elements and influences around you (besides family, friends, work, etc.). After the 28 days of recording, you'll find you can predict your energy/ moods and feelings, then use them to your benefit. (Some days more intuitive, some days more productive.)

See page 5 for the Energy of the Day reference chart.

Today's Galactic Body:

_____

What is the phase of the moon?

_____

What is the element of your location?
(Earth, Air, Fire, Water)

_____

What is the Energy of the Day today?

_____

What are today's colors?

_____

What is the weather today?
(Especially note extreme weather)

_____

How do you notice and respond to the Energy of the Day?
Draw, doodle, write, paste pictures/words.
Explore your way to express the Energy of the Day and perhaps your energy, too.

I chose this activity or activities to support my self-care today:

Week One - Day Seven

I am of service to those serving me.

I smile at the clerk at the store.

I am staying connected to the love when interacting with others.

Color, draw, doodle, and write about the above Daily Contemplation. Speak it out loud and to yourself to help internalize it. Include it in your daily meditation, walk or other practice. Notice when situations and circumstances arise where you can apply the Daily Contemplation.

What the Daily Contemplation Looks Like to Me:

How will you implement or integrate the Daily Contemplation today?

Week One

Wrap-Up and Review

**Please reflect (looking back at your pages from this week)
and answer the following:**

In what ways has the energy shifted for you this week?

Do you notice patterns from day to day when clearing the clutter from your mind?

List the ways you are more in touch with your Purpose and note Ah Ha's moments you've gotten this week:

Journal and reflect on the energies of the day, the self-care, and other new habits you've created:

Week One

Wrap-Up and Review

What are my top three Ah-Ha's from the past seven days?
1.

2.

3.

When was I the most proud in the past week?

Who have I served or loved this week as part of my Purpose?

How am I feeling about connecting with my Purpose?

Week Two

To help clear your mind and launch your week,
color, draw, doodle, and play with this weekly mandala...

Purpose is how I connect in the world

Week Two

Color and decorate your weekly intention. You might choose to add stickers or collage this page. If you wish, you can create a vision board around this intention. (As a reminder, a vision board is a visual prompt to help you focus on a specific goal or intention. You can use images that represent whatever this means to you.)

Internalize the intention by speaking it out loud and to yourself. Include the intention in your daily meditation, walk, or other practice. Ponder it through out the week.

This is the Weekly Intention:

Purpose is how I connect in the world

Everything you do relates to and supports this intention.
It is Big Picture Wisdom.
Be attentive to how it appears in your life this week.

Week Two

This is what the weekly intention looks like to you.
Draw, doodle, write, paste pictures – Create your vision of the weekly
intention.

My Daily Action Plan for the Week

- Start my day by breathing and grounding
- Remember and reflect upon the weekly intention
- Color, draw, doodle the daily mandala
- Do the Daily Mind Clearing
- Explore the Energy of the Day
- Review the Daily Contemplation, and capture how it manifest for me
- Allow time in my day to reflect and deepen my experience
- Listen to the SPARK Podcast to inspire and ground this weekly intention

Week Two

What Activities Support You?

Envision the next seven days.
What activities support and ground you as you move through the day?
What keeps you balanced, relieves stress and stimulates your creative juices?
Identify those activities on this list and add your own. If you like, post them in the Facebook group so everyone can share in the limitless supportive possibilities. Also capture those you would like to try someday.

This is not a commandment or a 'have-to must-do." It's an opportunity to explore self-care in whatever form that it works for you. We'll ask you every day to note what you did or what you plan to do. If it feels like too much pressure – skip it. Come back to it some other time when it feels right.

✓ Doing It   ● On the List Someday

- O Walk in Nature
- O Meditate / Be Still
- O Do Yoga or Stretch
- O Write or Journal
- O Nap or Sleep
- O Read a Book
- O Get a Massage or
- O Other Self Care
- O Cook & Eat a Healthy Meal
- O Go to the Gym
- O Run or Jog
- O Bike, Ski or Other Active Solo Sport
- O Play a Team Sport
- O Do Tai Chi or Qigong
- O Take Time for Your Hobby
- O Learn Something New
- O Play with Kids / Family
- O Devote Quality Time to Your Spouse
- O Connect With Friends
- O Connect With Pet(s)
- O Make Art / Be Creative
- O Organize or Clean Belongings
- O Sing or Make Music
- O Play an Instrument
- O Dance (Solo or with a Partner)
- O Get Wet (Swim, Paddle Board, Surf)
- O Take a Relaxing Bath

Week Two

During the weekly podcast, I offer tips and ideas to move even more deeply into your Purpose. Some weeks there are guest experts; we discuss everything from creativity, authenticity, and building your life on Purpose. There are also experts who use different tools to discover Purpose. I invite you to doodle, dream, and take notes while you listen – or come back later (if you listen in the car or elsewhere). Then jot down your thoughts here:

Weekly Podcast

Week Two

Weekly Podcast

Looking at your notes, what thoughts, ideas, and inspirations what do you want to capture from this week's SPARK: The Radically Authentic Life podcast?

- ☐ _____
- ☐ _____
- ☐ _____
- ☐ _____
- ☐ _____
- ☐ _____

Using these notes, what does it look like to you?
What ideas and thoughts of yours link to those from the podcast?
How are you inspired by what you heard?
Consider using thought bubbles to track the connections and flow.

Week Two - Day One

To help clear your mind and ground your day,
color, draw, doodle, and play with this daily mandala...

Briefly write about how you noticed Purpose was active in your life yesterday

Week Two - Day One

Intention: Purpose is how I connect in the world

Release the Mind From Clutter

What do I need to capture and then release from my mind, creating space so that I am open to possibilities?

Frustrations – Regrets – Sadness – Anger

Hopes – Dreams – Gratitude – Intentions

Plans – Want To's – Must Do's - Reminders

Draw, doodle, write, and do anything here for three minutes that helps clear your monkey-mind.
Then, if you want, brainstorm ways to organize them into your life.

Week Two - Day One

The Energy of the Day

Today, pay attention to all of the different elements and influences around you (besides family, friends, work, etc.). After the 28 days of recording, you'll find you can predict your energy/moods and feelings, then use them to your benefit. (Some days more intuitive, some days more productive.)

See page 5 for the Energy of the Day reference chart.

Today's Galactic Body:

_____

What is the phase of the moon?

_____

What is the element of your location?
(Earth, Air, Fire, Water)

_____

What is the Energy of the Day today?

_____

What are today's colors?

_____

What is the weather today?
(Especially note extreme weather)

_____

How do you notice and respond to the Energy of the Day?
Draw, doodle, write, paste pictures/words.
Explore your way to express the Energy of the Day and perhaps your energy, too.

I chose this activity or activities to support my self-care today:

Week Two - Day One

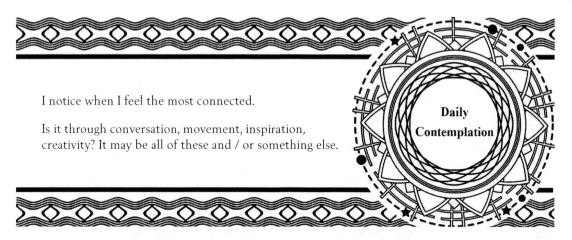

I notice when I feel the most connected.

Is it through conversation, movement, inspiration, creativity? It may be all of these and / or something else.

Daily Contemplation

Color, draw, doodle, and write about the above Daily Contemplation. Speak it out loud and to yourself to help internalize it. Include it in your daily meditation, walk or other practice. Notice when situations and circumstances arise where you can apply the Daily Contemplation.

What the Daily Contemplation Looks Like to Me:

How will you implement or integrate the Daily Contemplation today?

Week Two - Day Two

Day of the Week: _____   *Today's Date:* _____

To help clear your mind and ground your day,
color, draw, doodle, and play with this daily mandala...

Briefly write about how you noticed Purpose was active in your life yesterday

Week Two - Day Two

Intention: Purpose is how I connect in the world

Release the Mind From Clutter

What do I need to capture and then release from my mind, creating space so that I am open to possibilities?

Frustrations - Regrets - Sadness - Anger

Hopes – Dreams – Gratitude - Intentions

Plans – Want To's – Must Do's - Reminders

Draw, doodle, write, and do anything here for three minutes that helps clear your monkey-mind.
Then, if you want, brainstorm ways to organize them into your life.

Week Two - Day Two

The Energy of the Day

Today, pay attention to all of the different elements and influences around you (besides family, friends, work, etc.). After the 28 days of recording, you'll find you can predict your energy/moods and feelings, then use them to your benefit. (Some days more intuitive, some days more productive.)

See page 5 for the Energy of the Day reference chart.

Today's Galactic Body:

_____

What is the phase of the moon?

_____

What is the element of your location?
(Earth, Air, Fire, Water)

_____

What is the Energy of the Day today?

_____

What are today's colors?

_____

What is the weather today?
(Especially note extreme weather)

_____

How do you notice and respond to the Energy of the Day?
Draw, doodle, write, paste pictures/words.
Explore your way to express the Energy of the Day and perhaps your energy, too.

I chose this activity or activities to support my self-care today:

Week Two - Day Two

How do I want to feel when out in the world?

Daily Contemplation

Color, draw, doodle, and write about the above Daily Contemplation. Speak it out loud and to yourself to help internalize it. Include it in your daily meditation, walk or other practice. Notice when situations and circumstances arise where you can apply the Daily Contemplation.

What the Daily Contemplation Looks Like to Me:

How will you implement or integrate the Daily Contemplation today?

Week Two - Day Three

Day of the Week: _____   *Today's Date:* _____

To help clear your mind and ground your day,
color, draw, doodle, and play with this daily mandala...

Briefly write about how you noticed Purpose was active in your life yesterday

Week Two - Day Three

Intention: Purpose is how I connect in the world

Release the Mind From Clutter

What do I need to capture and then release from my mind, creating space so that I am open to possibilities?

Frustrations - Regrets - Sadness - Anger

Hopes – Dreams – Gratitude - Intentions

Plans – Want To's – Must Do's - Reminders

Draw, doodle, write, and do anything here for three minutes that helps clear your monkey-mind. Then, if you want, brainstorm ways to organize them into your life.

Week Two - Day Three

The Energy of the Day

Today, pay attention to all of the different elements and influences around you (besides family, friends, work, etc.). After the 28 days of recording, you'll find you can predict your energy/moods and feelings, then use them to your benefit. (Some days more intuitive, some days more productive.)

See page 5 for the Energy of the Day reference chart.

Today's Galactic Body:

_____

What is the phase of the moon?

_____

What is the element of your location?
(Earth, Air, Fire, Water)

_____

What is the Energy of the Day today?

_____

What are today's colors?

_____

What is the weather today?
(Especially note extreme weather)

_____

How do you notice and respond to the Energy of the Day?
Draw, doodle, write, paste pictures/words.
Explore your way to express the Energy of the Day and perhaps your energy, too.

I chose this activity or activities to support my self-care today:

Week Two - Day Three

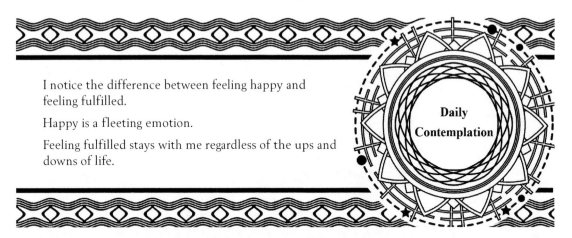

I notice the difference between feeling happy and feeling fulfilled.

Happy is a fleeting emotion.

Feeling fulfilled stays with me regardless of the ups and downs of life.

Daily Contemplation

Color, draw, doodle, and write about the above Daily Contemplation. Speak it out loud and to yourself to help internalize it. Include it in your daily meditation, walk or other practice. Notice when situations and circumstances arise where you can apply the Daily Contemplation.

What the Daily Contemplation Looks Like to Me:

How will you implement or integrate the Daily Contemplation today?

Week Two - Day Four

Day of the Week: _____   *Today's Date:* _____

To help clear your mind and ground your day,
color, draw, doodle, and play with this daily mandala...

Briefly write about how you noticed Purpose was active in your life yesterday

Week Two - Day Four

Intention: Purpose is how I connect in the world

Release the Mind From Clutter

*What do I need to capture and then release from my mind,
creating space so that I am open to possibilities?*

Frustrations - Regrets - Sadness - Anger

Hopes – Dreams – Gratitude - Intentions

Plans – Want To's – Must Do's - Reminders

Draw, doodle, write, and do anything here for three minutes that helps clear your monkey-mind.
Then, if you want, brainstorm ways to organize them into your life.

Week Two - Day Four

The Energy of the Day

Today, pay attention to all of the different elements and influences around you (besides family, friends, work, etc.). After the 28 days of recording, you'll find you can predict your energy/moods and feelings, then use them to your benefit. (Some days more intuitive, some days more productive.)

See page 5 for the Energy of the Day reference chart.

Today's Galactic Body:

_____

What is the Energy of the Day today?

_____

What is the phase of the moon?

_____

What are today's colors?

_____

What is the element of your location?
(Earth, Air, Fire, Water)

_____

What is the weather today?
(Especially note extreme weather)

_____

How do you notice and respond to the Energy of the Day?
Draw, doodle, write, paste pictures/words.
Explore your way to express the Energy of the Day and perhaps your energy, too.

I chose this activity or activities to support my self-care today:

Week Two - Day Four

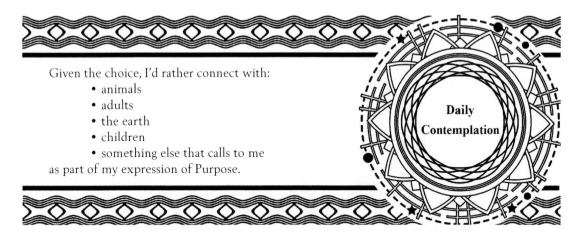

Given the choice, I'd rather connect with:
- animals
- adults
- the earth
- children
- something else that calls to me

as part of my expression of Purpose.

Daily Contemplation

Color, draw, doodle, and write about the above Daily Contemplation. Speak it out loud and to yourself to help internalize it. Include it in your daily meditation, walk or other practice. Notice when situations and circumstances arise where you can apply the Daily Contemplation.

What the Daily Contemplation Looks Like to Me:

How will you implement or integrate the Daily Contemplation today?

Week Two - Day Five

Day of the Week: _____   *Today's Date:* _____

To help clear your mind and ground your day,
color, draw, doodle, and play with this daily mandala...

Briefly write about how you noticed Purpose was active in your life yesterday

Week Two - Day Five

Intention: Purpose is how I connect in the world

Release the Mind From Clutter

*What do I need to capture and then release from my mind,
creating space so that I am open to possibilities?*

Frustrations - Regrets - Sadness - Anger

Hopes – Dreams – Gratitude - Intentions

Plans – Want To's – Must Do's - Reminders

Draw, doodle, write, and do anything here for three minutes that helps clear your monkey-mind.
Then, if you want, brainstorm ways to organize them into your life.

Week Two - Day Five

The Energy of the Day

Today, pay attention to all of the different elements and influences around you (besides family, friends, work, etc.). After the 28 days of recording, you'll find you can predict your energy/ moods and feelings, then use them to your benefit. (Some days more intuitive, some days more productive.)

See page 5 for the Energy of the Day reference chart.

Today's Galactic Body:

_____

What is the phase of the moon?

_____

What is the element of your location?
(Earth, Air, Fire, Water)

_____

What is the Energy of the Day today?

_____

What are today's colors?

_____

What is the weather today?
(Especially note extreme weather)

_____

How do you notice and respond to the Energy of the Day?
Draw, doodle, write, paste pictures/words.
Explore your way to express the Energy of the Day and perhaps your energy, too.

I chose this activity or activities to support my self-care today:

Week Two - Day Five

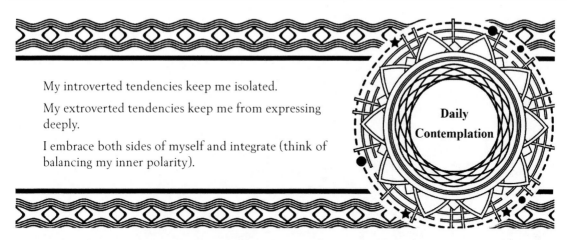

My introverted tendencies keep me isolated.

My extroverted tendencies keep me from expressing deeply.

I embrace both sides of myself and integrate (think of balancing my inner polarity).

Daily Contemplation

Color, draw, doodle, and write about the above Daily Contemplation. Speak it out loud and to yourself to help internalize it. Include it in your daily meditation, walk or other practice. Notice when situations and circumstances arise where you can apply the Daily Contemplation.

What the Daily Contemplation Looks Like to Me:

How will you implement or integrate the Daily Contemplation today?

Week Two - Day Six

Day of the Week: _____   *Today's Date:* _____

To help clear your mind and ground your day,
color, draw, doodle, and play with this daily mandala...

Briefly write about how you noticed Purpose was active in your life yesterday

Week Two - Day Six

Intention: Purpose is how I connect in the world

Release the Mind From Clutter

What do I need to capture and then release from my mind, creating space so that I am open to possibilities?

Frustrations - Regrets - Sadness - Anger

Hopes – Dreams – Gratitude - Intentions

Plans – Want To's – Must Do's - Reminders

Draw, doodle, write, and do anything here for three minutes that helps clear your monkey-mind. Then, if you want, brainstorm ways to organize them into your life.

Week Two - Day Six

The Energy of the Day

Today, pay attention to all of the different elements and influences around you (besides family, friends, work, etc.). After the 28 days of recording, you'll find you can predict your energy/ moods and feelings, then use them to your benefit. (Some days more intuitive, some days more productive.)

See page 5 for the Energy of the Day reference chart.

Today's Galactic Body:

_____

What is the phase of the moon?

_____

What is the element of your location?
(Earth, Air, Fire, Water)

_____

What is the Energy of the Day today?

_____

What are today's colors?

_____

What is the weather today?
(Especially note extreme weather)

_____

How do you notice and respond to the Energy of the Day?
Draw, doodle, write, paste pictures/words.
Explore your way to express the Energy of the Day and perhaps your energy, too.

I chose this activity or activities to support my self-care today:

Week Two - Day Six

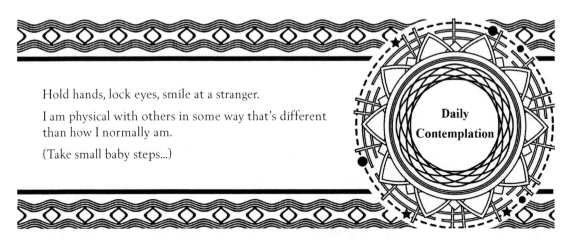

Hold hands, lock eyes, smile at a stranger.

I am physical with others in some way that's different than how I normally am.

(Take small baby steps...)

Daily Contemplation

Color, draw, doodle, and write about the above Daily Contemplation. Speak it out loud and to yourself to help internalize it. Include it in your daily meditation, walk or other practice. Notice when situations and circumstances arise where you can apply the Daily Contemplation.

What the Daily Contemplation Looks Like to Me:

How will you implement or integrate the Daily Contemplation today?

Week Two - Day Seven

Day of the Week: _____   *Today's Date:* _____

To help clear your mind and ground your day,
color, draw, doodle, and play with this daily mandala...

Briefly write about how you noticed Purpose was active in your life yesterday

Week Two - Day Seven

Intention: Purpose is how I connect in the world

Release the Mind From Clutter

What do I need to capture and then release from my mind, creating space so that I am open to possibilities?

Frustrations - Regrets - Sadness - Anger

Hopes – Dreams – Gratitude - Intentions

Plans – Want To's – Must Do's - Reminders

Draw, doodle, write, and do anything here for three minutes that helps clear your monkey-mind. Then, if you want, brainstorm ways to organize them into your life.

Week Two - Day Seven

The Energy of the Day

Today, pay attention to all of the different elements and influences around you (besides family, friends, work, etc.). After the 28 days of recording, you'll find you can predict your energy/moods and feelings, then use them to your benefit. (Some days more intuitive, some days more productive.)

See page 5 for the Energy of the Day reference chart.

Today's Galactic Body:

_____

What is the phase of the moon?

_____

What is the element of your location?
(Earth, Air, Fire, Water)

_____

What is the Energy of the Day today?

_____

What are today's colors?

_____

What is the weather today?
(Especially note extreme weather)

_____

How do you notice and respond to the Energy of the Day?
Draw, doodle, write, paste pictures/words.
Explore your way to express the Energy of the Day and perhaps your energy, too.

I chose this activity or activities to support my self-care today:

Week Two - Day Seven

How do I stay grounded and in service? (Hint: Don't take on other people's heartaches, just love them where they are as they are.)

Daily Contemplation

Color, draw, doodle, and write about the above Daily Contemplation. Speak it out loud and to yourself to help internalize it. Include it in your daily meditation, walk or other practice. Notice when situations and circumstances arise where you can apply the Daily Contemplation.

What the Daily Contemplation Looks Like to Me:

How will you implement or integrate the Daily Contemplation today?

Week Two

Wrap-Up and Review

**Please reflect (looking back at your pages from this week)
and answer the following:**

In what ways has the energy shifted for you this week?

Do you notice patterns from day to day when clearing the clutter from your mind?

List the ways you are more in touch with your Purpose and note Ah Ha's moments you've gotten this week:

Journal and reflect on the energies of the day, the self-care, and other new habits you've created:

Week Two

Wrap-Up and Review

What are my top three Ah-Ha's from the past seven days?

1.

2.

3.

When was I the most proud in past week?

Who have I served or loved this week as part of my Purpose?

How am I feeling about connecting with my Purpose?

Week Three

To help clear your mind and launch your week,
color, draw, doodle, and play with this weekly mandala...

Purpose is how I serve and share my love

Week Three

Color and decorate your weekly intention. You might choose to add stickers or collage this page. If you wish, you can create a vision board around this intention. (As a reminder, a vision board is a visual prompt to help you focus on a specific goal or intention. You can use images that represent whatever this means to you.)

Internalize the intention by speaking it out loud and to yourself. Include the intention in your daily meditation, walk, or other practice. Ponder it through out the week.

This is the Weekly Intention:

Purpose is how I serve and share my love

Everything you do relates to and supports this intention.
It is Big Picture Wisdom.
Be attentive to how it appears in your life this week.

Week Three

This is what the weekly intention looks like to you.
Draw, doodle, write, paste pictures – Create your vision of the weekly intention.

My Daily Action Plan for the Week

- Start my day by breathing and grounding
- Remember and reflect upon the weekly intention
- Color, draw, doodle the daily mandala
- Do the Daily Mind Clearing
- Explore the Energy of the Day
- Review the Daily Contemplation, and capture how it manifest for me
- Allow time in my day to reflect and deepen my experience
- Listen to the SPARK Podcast to inspire and ground this weekly intention

Week Three

What Activities Support You?

Envision the next seven days.
What activities support and ground you as you move through the day?
What keeps you balanced, relieves stress and stimulates your creative juices?
Identify those activities on this list and add your own. If you like, post them in the Facebook group so everyone can share in the limitless supportive possibilities. Also capture those you would like to try someday.

This is not a commandment or a 'have-to must-do." It's an opportunity to explore self-care in whatever form that it works for you. We'll ask you every day to note what you did or what you plan to do. If it feels like too much pressure – skip it. Come back to it some other time when it feels right.

✓ Doing It   ● On the List Someday

- O Walk in Nature
- O Meditate / Be Still
- O Do Yoga or Stretch
- O Write or Journal
- O Nap or Sleep
- O Read a Book
- O Get a Massage or
- O Other Self Care
- O Cook & Eat a Healthy Meal
- O Go to the Gym
- O Run or Jog
- O Bike, Ski or Other Active Solo Sport
- O Play a Team Sport
- O Do Tai Chi or Qigong
- O Take Time for Your Hobby
- O Learn Something New
- O Play with Kids / Family
- O Devote Quality Time to Your Spouse
- O Connect With Friends
- O Connect With Pet(s)
- O Make Art / Be Creative
- O Organize or Clean Belongings
- O Sing or Make Music
- O Play an Instrument
- O Dance (Solo or with a Partner)
- O Get Wet (Swim, Paddle Board, Surf)
- O Take a Relaxing Bath

Week Three

During the weekly podcast, I offer tips and ideas to move even more deeply into your Purpose. Some weeks there are guest experts; we discuss everything from creativity, authenticity, and building your life on Purpose. There are also experts who use different tools to discover Purpose. I invite you to doodle, dream, and take notes while you listen – or come back later (if you listen in the car or elsewhere). Then jot down your thoughts here:

Weekly Podcast

Week Three

Weekly Podcast

Looking at your notes, what thoughts, ideas, and inspirations what do you want to capture from this week's SPARK: The Radically Authentic Life podcast?

☐ _____

☐ _____

☐ _____

☐ _____

☐ _____

☐ _____

Using these notes, what does it look like to you?
What ideas and thoughts of yours link to those from the podcast?
How are you inspired by what you heard?
Consider using thought bubbles to track the connections and flow.

Week Three - Day One

Day of the Week: _____   *Today's Date:* _____

To help clear your mind and ground your day,
color, draw, doodle, and play with this daily mandala...

Briefly write about how you noticed Purpose was active in your life yesterday

Week Three - Day One

Intention: *Purpose is how I serve and share my love*

Release the Mind From Clutter

*What do I need to capture and then release from my mind,
creating space so that I am open to possibilities?*

Frustrations - Regrets - Sadness - Anger

Hopes – Dreams – Gratitude - Intentions

Plans – Want To's – Must Do's - Reminders

Draw, doodle, write, and do anything here for three minutes that helps clear your monkey-mind.
Then, if you want, brainstorm ways to organize them into your life.

Week Three - Day One

The Energy of the Day

Today, pay attention to all of the different elements and influences around you (besides family, friends, work, etc.). After the 28 days of recording, you'll find you can predict your energy/moods and feelings, then use them to your benefit. (Some days more intuitive, some days more productive.)

See page 5 for the Energy of the Day reference chart.

Today's Galactic Body:

_____

What is the phase of the moon?

_____

What is the element of your location?
(Earth, Air, Fire, Water)

_____

What is the Energy of the Day today?

_____

What are today's colors?

_____

What is the weather today?
(Especially note extreme weather)

_____

How do you notice and respond to the Energy of the Day?
Draw, doodle, write, paste pictures/words.
Explore your way to express the Energy of the Day and perhaps your energy, too.

I chose this activity or activities to support my self-care today:

Week Three - Day One

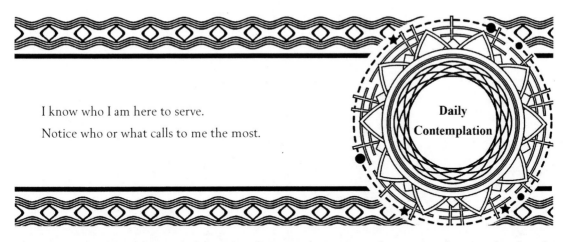

I know who I am here to serve.

Notice who or what calls to me the most.

Daily Contemplation

Color, draw, doodle, and write about the above Daily Contemplation. Speak it out loud and to yourself to help internalize it. Include it in your daily meditation, walk or other practice. Notice when situations and circumstances arise where you can apply the Daily Contemplation.

What the Daily Contemplation Looks Like to Me:

How will you implement or integrate the Daily Contemplation today?

Week Three - Day Two

Day of the Week: _____   *Today's Date:* _____

To help clear your mind and ground your day,
color, draw, doodle, and play with this daily mandala...

Briefly write about how you noticed Purpose was active in your life yesterday

Week Three - Day Two

Intention: Purpose is how I serve and share my love

Release the Mind From Clutter

What do I need to capture and then release from my mind, creating space so that I am open to possibilities?

Frustrations - Regrets - Sadness - Anger

Hopes – Dreams – Gratitude - Intentions

Plans – Want To's – Must Do's - Reminders

Draw, doodle, write, and do anything here for three minutes that helps clear your monkey-mind. Then, if you want, brainstorm ways to organize them into your life.

Week Three - Day Two

The Energy of the Day

Today, pay attention to all of the different elements and influences around you (besides family, friends, work, etc.). After the 28 days of recording, you'll find you can predict your energy/ moods and feelings, then use them to your benefit. (Some days more intuitive, some days more productive.)

See page 5 for the Energy of the Day reference chart.

Today's Galactic Body:

_____

What is the phase of the moon?

_____

What is the element of your location?
(Earth, Air, Fire, Water)

_____

What is the Energy of the Day today?

_____

What are today's colors?

_____

What is the weather today?
(Especially note extreme weather)

_____

How do you notice and respond to the Energy of the Day?
Draw, doodle, write, paste pictures/words.
Explore your way to express the Energy of the Day and perhaps your energy, too.

I chose this activity or activities to support my self-care today:

Week Three - Day Two

I notice what form my services takes.

How does it look in the world?

Daily Contemplation

Color, draw, doodle, and write about the above Daily Contemplation. Speak it out loud and to yourself to help internalize it. Include it in your daily meditation, walk or other practice. Notice when situations and circumstances arise where you can apply the Daily Contemplation.

What the Daily Contemplation Looks Like to Me:

How will you implement or integrate the Daily Contemplation today?

Week Three - Day Three

Day of the Week: _____   *Today's Date:* _____

To help clear your mind and ground your day,
color, draw, doodle, and play with this daily mandala...

Briefly write about how you noticed Purpose was active in your life yesterday

Week Three - Day Three

Intention: Purpose is how I serve and share my love

Release the Mind From Clutter

What do I need to capture and then release from my mind, creating space so that I am open to possibilities?

Frustrations - Regrets - Sadness - Anger

Hopes – Dreams – Gratitude - Intentions

Plans – Want To's – Must Do's - Reminders

Draw, doodle, write, and do anything here for three minutes that helps clear your monkey-mind.
Then, if you want, brainstorm ways to organize them into your life.

Week Three - Day Three

The Energy of the Day

Today, pay attention to all of the different elements and influences around you (besides family, friends, work, etc.). After the 28 days of recording, you'll find you can predict your energy/ moods and feelings, then use them to your benefit. (Some days more intuitive, some days more productive.)

See page 5 for the Energy of the Day reference chart.

Today's Galactic Body:

_____

What is the phase of the moon?

_____

What is the element of your location?
(Earth, Air, Fire, Water)

_____

What is the Energy of the Day today?

_____

What are today's colors?

_____

What is the weather today?
(Especially note extreme weather)

_____

How do you notice and respond to the Energy of the Day?
Draw, doodle, write, paste pictures/words.
Explore your way to express the Energy of the Day and perhaps your energy, too.

I chose this activity or activities to support my self-care today:

Week Three - Day Three

I notice what happens when I speak my truth while in service to others.

I am open in my heart.

Daily Contemplation

Color, draw, doodle, and write about the above Daily Contemplation. Speak it out loud and to yourself to help internalize it. Include it in your daily meditation, walk or other practice. Notice when situations and circumstances arise where you can apply the Daily Contemplation.

What the Daily Contemplation Looks Like to Me:

How will you implement or integrate the Daily Contemplation today?

Week Three - Day Four

Day of the Week: _____   *Today's Date:* _____

To help clear your mind and ground your day,
color, draw, doodle, and play with this daily mandala...

Briefly write about how you noticed Purpose was active in your life yesterday

Week Three - Day Four

Intention: Purpose is how I serve and share my love

Release the Mind From Clutter

What do I need to capture and then release from my mind, creating space so that I am open to possibilities?

Frustrations - Regrets - Sadness - Anger

Hopes – Dreams – Gratitude - Intentions

Plans – Want To's – Must Do's - Reminders

Draw, doodle, write, and do anything here for three minutes that helps clear your monkey-mind. Then, if you want, brainstorm ways to organize them into your life.

Week Three - Day Four

The Energy of the Day

Today, pay attention to all of the different elements and influences around you (besides family, friends, work, etc.). After the 28 days of recording, you'll find you can predict your energy/moods and feelings, then use them to your benefit. (Some days more intuitive, some days more productive.)

See page 5 for the Energy of the Day reference chart.

Today's Galactic Body:

_____

What is the phase of the moon?

_____

What is the element of your location?
(Earth, Air, Fire, Water)

_____

What is the Energy of the Day today?

_____

What are today's colors?

_____

What is the weather today?
(Especially note extreme weather)

_____

How do you notice and respond to the Energy of the Day?
Draw, doodle, write, paste pictures/words.
Explore your way to express the Energy of the Day and perhaps your energy, too.

I chose this activity or activities to support my self-care today:

Week Three - Day Four

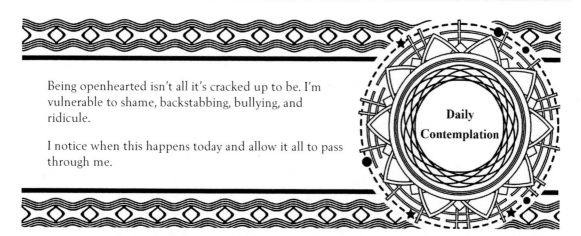

Daily Contemplation

Being openhearted isn't all it's cracked up to be. I'm vulnerable to shame, backstabbing, bullying, and ridicule.

I notice when this happens today and allow it all to pass through me.

Color, draw, doodle, and write about the above Daily Contemplation. Speak it out loud and to yourself to help internalize it. Include it in your daily meditation, walk or other practice. Notice when situations and circumstances arise where you can apply the Daily Contemplation.

What the Daily Contemplation Looks Like to Me:

How will you implement or integrate the Daily Contemplation today?

Week Three - Day Five

Day of the Week: _____   *Today's Date:* _____

To help clear your mind and ground your day,
color, draw, doodle, and play with this daily mandala...

Briefly write about how you noticed Purpose was active in your life yesterday

126

Week Three - Day Five

Intention: Purpose is how I serve and share my love

Release the Mind From Clutter

What do I need to capture and then release from my mind, creating space so that I am open to possibilities?

Frustrations - Regrets - Sadness - Anger

Hopes – Dreams – Gratitude - Intentions

Plans – Want To's – Must Do's - Reminders

Draw, doodle, write, and do anything here for three minutes that helps clear your monkey-mind.
Then, if you want, brainstorm ways to organize them into your life.

127

Week Three - Day Five

The Energy of the Day

Today, pay attention to all of the different elements and influences around you (besides family, friends, work, etc.). After the 28 days of recording, you'll find you can predict your energy/ moods and feelings, then use them to your benefit. (Some days more intuitive, some days more productive.)

See page 5 for the Energy of the Day reference chart.

Today's Galactic Body:

_____

What is the phase of the moon?

_____

What is the element of your location?
(Earth, Air, Fire, Water)

_____

What is the Energy of the Day today?

_____

What are today's colors?

_____

What is the weather today?
(Especially note extreme weather)

_____

How do you notice and respond to the Energy of the Day?
Draw, doodle, write, paste pictures/words.
Explore your way to express the Energy of the Day and perhaps your energy, too.

I chose this activity or activities to support my self-care today:

Week Three - Day Five

What if my heart was fearless?

Daily Contemplation

Color, draw, doodle, and write about the above Daily Contemplation. Speak it out loud and to yourself to help internalize it. Include it in your daily meditation, walk or other practice. Notice when situations and circumstances arise where you can apply the Daily Contemplation.

What the Daily Contemplation Looks Like to Me:

How will you implement or integrate the Daily Contemplation today?

Week Three - Day Six

Day of the Week: _____   *Today's Date:* _____

To help clear your mind and ground your day,
color, draw, doodle, and play with this daily mandala...

Briefly write about how you noticed Purpose was active in your life yesterday

Week Three - Day Six

Intention: Purpose is how I serve and share my love

Release the Mind From Clutter

What do I need to capture and then release from my mind, creating space so that I am open to possibilities?

Frustrations - Regrets - Sadness - Anger

Hopes – Dreams – Gratitude - Intentions

Plans – Want To's – Must Do's - Reminders

Draw, doodle, write, and do anything here for three minutes that helps clear your monkey-mind.
Then, if you want, brainstorm ways to organize them into your life.

Week Three - Day Six

The Energy of the Day

Today, pay attention to all of the different elements and influences around you (besides family, friends, work, etc.). After the 28 days of recording, you'll find you can predict your energy/ moods and feelings, then use them to your benefit. (Some days more intuitive, some days more productive.)

See page 5 for the Energy of the Day reference chart.

Today's Galactic Body:

_____

What is the phase of the moon?

_____

What is the element of your location?
(Earth, Air, Fire, Water)

_____

What is the Energy of the Day today?

_____

What are today's colors?

_____

What is the weather today?
(Especially note extreme weather)

_____

How do you notice and respond to the Energy of the Day?
Draw, doodle, write, paste pictures/words.
Explore your way to express the Energy of the Day and perhaps your energy, too.

I chose this activity or activities to support my self-care today:

Week Three - Day Six

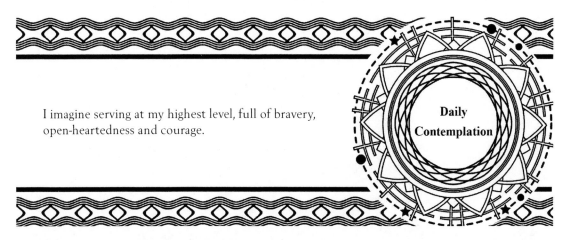

I imagine serving at my highest level, full of bravery, open-heartedness and courage.

Daily Contemplation

Color, draw, doodle, and write about the above Daily Contemplation. Speak it out loud and to yourself to help internalize it. Include it in your daily meditation, walk or other practice. Notice when situations and circumstances arise where you can apply the Daily Contemplation.

What the Daily Contemplation Looks Like to Me:

How will you implement or integrate the Daily Contemplation today?

Week Three - Day Seven

Day of the Week: _____   *Today's Date:* _____

To help clear your mind and ground your day,
color, draw, doodle, and play with this daily mandala...

Briefly write about how you noticed Purpose was active in your life yesterday

Week Three - Day Seven

Intention: Purpose is how I serve and share my love

Release the Mind From Clutter

What do I need to capture and then release from my mind, creating space so that I am open to possibilities?

Frustrations - Regrets - Sadness - Anger

Hopes – Dreams – Gratitude - Intentions

Plans – Want To's – Must Do's - Reminders

Draw, doodle, write, and do anything here for three minutes that helps clear your monkey-mind. Then, if you want, brainstorm ways to organize them into your life.

Week Three - Day Seven

The Energy of the Day

Today, pay attention to all of the different elements and influences around you (besides family, friends, work, etc.). After the 28 days of recording, you'll find you can predict your energy/ moods and feelings, then use them to your benefit. (Some days more intuitive, some days more productive.)

See page 5 for the Energy of the Day reference chart.

Today's Galactic Body:

_____

What is the phase of the moon?

_____

What is the element of your location?
(Earth, Air, Fire, Water)

_____

What is the Energy of the Day today?

_____

What are today's colors?

_____

What is the weather today?
(Especially note extreme weather)

_____

How do you notice and respond to the Energy of the Day?
Draw, doodle, write, paste pictures/words.
Explore your way to express the Energy of the Day and perhaps your energy, too.

I chose this activity or activities to support my self-care today:

Week Three - Day Seven

I do one nice thing for someone I'm here to serve.

It will be a totally unexpected bonus, with no expectation, just fearless open heart.

Daily
Contemplation

Color, draw, doodle, and write about the above Daily Contemplation. Speak it out loud and to yourself to help internalize it. Include it in your daily meditation, walk or other practice. Notice when situations and circumstances arise where you can apply the Daily Contemplation.

What the Daily Contemplation Looks Like to Me:

How will you implement or integrate the Daily Contemplation today?

Week Three

Wrap-Up and Review

**Please reflect (looking back at your pages from this week)
and answer the following:**

In what ways has the energy shifted for you this week?

Do you notice patterns from day to day when clearing the clutter from your mind?

List the ways you are more in touch with your Purpose and note Ah Ha's moments you've gotten this week:

Journal and reflect on the energies of the day, the self-care, and other new habits you've created:

Week Three

Wrap-Up and Review

What are my top three Ah-Ha's from the past seven days?

1.

2.

3.

When was I the most proud in the past week?

Who have I served or loved this week as part of my Purpose?

How am I feeling about connecting with my Purpose?

Week Four

To help clear your mind and launch your week,
color, draw, doodle, and play with this weekly mandala...

I see the Purpose in my life

Week Four

Color and decorate your weekly intention. You might choose to add stickers or collage this page. If you wish, you can create a vision board around this intention. (As a reminder, a vision board is a visual prompt to help you focus on a specific goal or intention. You can use images that represent whatever this means to you.)

Internalize the intention by speaking it out loud and to yourself. Include the intention in your daily meditation, walk, or other practice. Ponder it through out the week.

This is the Weekly Intention:

I

see the

Purpose

in my life

Everything you do relates to and supports this intention.
It is Big Picture Wisdom.
Be attentive to how it appears in your life this week.

Week Four

This is what the weekly intention looks like to you.
Draw, doodle, write, paste pictures – Create your vision of the weekly intention.

My Daily Action Plan for the Week

- Start my day by breathing and grounding
- Remember and reflect upon the weekly intention
- Color, draw, doodle the daily mandala
- Do the Daily Mind Clearing
- Explore the Energy of the Day
- Review the Daily Contemplation, and capture how it manifest for me
- Allow time in my day to reflect and deepen my experience
- Listen to the SPARK Podcast to inspire and ground this weekly intention

Week Four

What Activities Support You?

Envision the next seven days.
What activities support and ground you as you move through the day?
What keeps you balanced, relieves stress and stimulates your creative juices?
Identify those activities on this list and add your own. If you like, post them in the Facebook group so everyone can share in the limitless supportive possibilities. Also capture those you would like to try someday.

This is not a commandment or a 'have-to must-do." It's an opportunity to explore self-care in whatever form that it works for you. We'll ask you every day to note what you did or what you plan to do. If it feels like too much pressure – skip it. Come back to it some other time when it feels right.

✓ Doing It   ● On the List Someday

- ○ Walk in Nature
- ○ Meditate / Be Still
- ○ Do Yoga or Stretch
- ○ Write or Journal
- ○ Nap or Sleep
- ○ Read a Book
- ○ Get a Massage or
- ○ Other Self Care
- ○ Cook & Eat a Healthy Meal
- ○ Go to the Gym
- ○ Run or Jog
- ○ Bike, Ski or Other Active Solo Sport
- ○ Play a Team Sport
- ○ Do Tai Chi or Qigong
- ○ Take Time for Your Hobby
- ○ Learn Something New

- ○ Play with Kids / Family
- ○ Devote Quality Time to Your Spouse
- ○ Connect With Friends
- ○ Connect With Pet(s)
- ○ Make Art / Be Creative
- ○ Organize or Clean Belongings
- ○ Sing or Make Music
- ○ Play an Instrument
- ○ Dance (Solo or with a Partner)
- ○ Get Wet (Swim, Paddle Board, Surf)
- ○ Take a Relaxing Bath

Week Four

During the weekly podcast, I offer tips and ideas to move even more deeply into your Purpose. Some weeks there are guest experts; we discuss everything from creativity, authenticity, and building your life on Purpose. There are also experts who use different tools to discover Purpose. I invite you to doodle, dream, and take notes while you listen – or come back later (if you listen in the car or elsewhere). Then jot down your thoughts here:

Weekly Podcast

Week Four

Weekly Podcast

Looking at your notes, what thoughts, ideas, and inspirations what do you want to capture from this week's SPARK: The Radically Authentic Life podcast?

- ☐ _____
- ☐ _____
- ☐ _____
- ☐ _____
- ☐ _____
- ☐ _____

Using these notes, what does it look like to you?
What ideas and thoughts of yours link to those from the podcast?
How are you inspired by what you heard?
Consider using thought bubbles to track the connections and flow.

Week Four - Day One

Day of the Week: _____   *Today's Date:* _____

To help clear your mind and ground your day,
color, draw, doodle, and play with this daily mandala...

Briefly write about how you noticed Purpose was active in your life yesterday

Week Four - Day One

Intention: I see the Purpose in my life

Release the Mind From Clutter

What do I need to capture and then release from my mind, creating space so that I am open to possibilities?

Frustrations - Regrets - Sadness - Anger

Hopes – Dreams – Gratitude - Intentions

Plans – Want To's – Must Do's - Reminders

Draw, doodle, write, and do anything here for three minutes that helps clear your monkey-mind.
Then, if you want, brainstorm ways to organize them into your life.

147

Week Four - Day One

The Energy of the Day

Today, pay attention to all of the different elements and influences around you (besides family, friends, work, etc.). After the 28 days of recording, you'll find you can predict your energy/ moods and feelings, then use them to your benefit. (Some days more intuitive, some days more productive.)

See page 5 for the Energy of the Day reference chart.

Today's Galactic Body:

_____

What is the phase of the moon?

_____

What is the element of your location?
(Earth, Air, Fire, Water)

_____

What is the Energy of the Day today?

_____

What are today's colors?

_____

What is the weather today?
(Especially note extreme weather)

_____

How do you notice and respond to the Energy of the Day?
Draw, doodle, write, paste pictures/words.
Explore your way to express the Energy of the Day and perhaps your energy, too.

I chose this activity or activities to support my self-care today:

Week Four - Day One

Just *Be*-ing alive is the greatest Purpose of all.

Notice it.

Daily Contemplation

Color, draw, doodle, and write about the above Daily Contemplation. Speak it out loud and to yourself to help internalize it. Include it in your daily meditation, walk or other practice. Notice when situations and circumstances arise where you can apply the Daily Contemplation.

What the Daily Contemplation Looks Like to Me:

How will you implement or integrate the Daily Contemplation today?

Week Four - Day Two

Day of the Week: _____   *Today's Date:* _____

To help clear your mind and ground your day,
color, draw, doodle, and play with this daily mandala...

Briefly write about how you noticed Purpose was active in your life yesterday

Week Four - Day Two

Intention: I see the Purpose in my life

Release the Mind From Clutter

What do I need to capture and then release from my mind, creating space so that I am open to possibilities?

Frustrations - Regrets - Sadness - Anger

Hopes – Dreams – Gratitude - Intentions

Plans – Want To's – Must Do's - Reminders

Draw, doodle, write, and do anything here for three minutes that helps clear your monkey-mind.
Then, if you want, brainstorm ways to organize them into your life.

151

Week Four - Day Two

The Energy of the Day

Today, pay attention to all of the different elements and influences around you (besides family, friends, work, etc.). After the 28 days of recording, you'll find you can predict your energy/moods and feelings, then use them to your benefit. (Some days more intuitive, some days more productive.)

See page 5 for the Energy of the Day reference chart.

Today's Galactic Body:

_____

What is the phase of the moon?

_____

What is the element of your location?
(Earth, Air, Fire, Water)

_____

What is the Energy of the Day today?

_____

What are today's colors?

_____

What is the weather today?
(Especially note extreme weather)

_____

How do you notice and respond to the Energy of the Day?
Draw, doodle, write, paste pictures/words.
Explore your way to express the Energy of the Day and perhaps your energy, too.

I chose this activity or activities to support my self-care today:

Week Four - Day Two

In the stillness of life, I honor the Purpose of those around me.

Daily Contemplation

Color, draw, doodle, and write about the above Daily Contemplation. Speak it out loud and to yourself to help internalize it. Include it in your daily meditation, walk or other practice. Notice when situations and circumstances arise where you can apply the Daily Contemplation.

What the Daily Contemplation Looks Like to Me:

How will you implement or integrate the Daily Contemplation today?

Week Four - Day Three

Day of the Week: _____   *Today's Date:* _____

To help clear your mind and ground your day,
color, draw, doodle, and play with this daily mandala...

Briefly write about how you noticed Purpose was active in your life yesterday

Week Four - Day Three

Intention: I see the Purpose in my life

Release the Mind From Clutter

What do I need to capture and then release from my mind, creating space so that I am open to possibilities?

Frustrations - Regrets - Sadness - Anger

Hopes – Dreams – Gratitude - Intentions

Plans – Want To's – Must Do's - Reminders

Draw, doodle, write, and do anything here for three minutes that helps clear your monkey-mind. Then, if you want, brainstorm ways to organize them into your life.

Week Four - Day Three

The Energy of the Day

Today, pay attention to all of the different elements and influences around you (besides family, friends, work, etc.). After the 28 days of recording, you'll find you can predict your energy/moods and feelings, then use them to your benefit. (Some days more intuitive, some days more productive.)

See page 5 for the Energy of the Day reference chart.

Today's Galactic Body:

_____

What is the phase of the moon?

_____

What is the element of your location?
(Earth, Air, Fire, Water)

_____

What is the Energy of the Day today?

_____

What are today's colors?

_____

What is the weather today?
(Especially note extreme weather)

_____

How do you notice and respond to the Energy of the Day?
Draw, doodle, write, paste pictures/words.
Explore your way to express the Energy of the Day and perhaps your energy, too.

I chose this activity or activities to support my self-care today:

Week Four - Day Three

Understanding that my Purpose is already inside me and is expressing daily, what does it look like today?

Daily Contemplation

Color, draw, doodle, and write about the above Daily Contemplation. Speak it out loud and to yourself to help internalize it. Include it in your daily meditation, walk or other practice. Notice when situations and circumstances arise where you can apply the Daily Contemplation.

What the Daily Contemplation Looks Like to Me:

How will you implement or integrate the Daily Contemplation today?

Week Four - Day Four

Day of the Week: _____   *Today's Date:* _____

To help clear your mind and ground your day,
color, draw, doodle, and play with this daily mandala...

Briefly write about how you noticed Purpose was active in your life yesterday

Week Four - Day Four

Intention: I see the Purpose in my life

Release the Mind From Clutter

What do I need to capture and then release from my mind, creating space so that I am open to possibilities?

Frustrations - Regrets - Sadness - Anger

Hopes – Dreams – Gratitude - Intentions

Plans – Want To's – Must Do's - Reminders

Draw, doodle, write, and do anything here for three minutes that helps clear your monkey-mind. Then, if you want, brainstorm ways to organize them into your life.

159

Week Four - Day Four

The Energy of the Day

Today, pay attention to all of the different elements and influences around you (besides family, friends, work, etc.). After the 28 days of recording, you'll find you can predict your energy/moods and feelings, then use them to your benefit. (Some days more intuitive, some days more productive.)

See page 5 for the Energy of the Day reference chart.

Today's Galactic Body: What is the Energy of the Day today?

_____   _____

What is the phase of the moon?   What are today's colors?

_____   _____

What is the element of your location?   What is the weather today?
(Earth, Air, Fire, Water)   (Especially note extreme weather)

_____   _____

How do you notice and respond to the Energy of the Day?
Draw, doodle, write, paste pictures/words.
Explore your way to express the Energy of the Day and perhaps your energy, too.

I chose this activity or activities to support my self-care today:

Week Four - Day Four

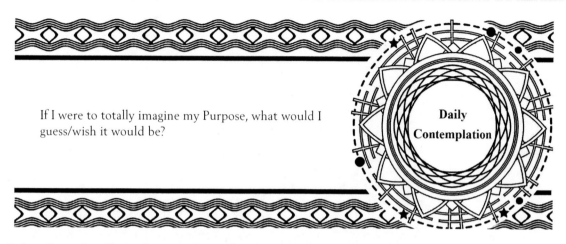

If I were to totally imagine my Purpose, what would I guess/wish it would be?

Daily Contemplation

Color, draw, doodle, and write about the above Daily Contemplation. Speak it out loud and to yourself to help internalize it. Include it in your daily meditation, walk or other practice. Notice when situations and circumstances arise where you can apply the Daily Contemplation.

What the Daily Contemplation Looks Like to Me:

How will you implement or integrate the Daily Contemplation today?

Week Four - Day Five

Day of the Week: _____   *Today's Date:* _____

To help clear your mind and ground your day,
color, draw, doodle, and play with this daily mandala...

Briefly write about how you noticed Purpose was active in your life yesterday

Week Four - Day Five

Intention: I see the Purpose in my life

Release the Mind From Clutter

What do I need to capture and then release from my mind, creating space so that I am open to possibilities?

Frustrations - Regrets - Sadness - Anger

Hopes – Dreams – Gratitude - Intentions

Plans – Want To's – Must Do's - Reminders

Draw, doodle, write, and do anything here for three minutes that helps clear your monkey-mind.
Then, if you want, brainstorm ways to organize them into your life.

Week Four - Day Five

The Energy of the Day

Today, pay attention to all of the different elements and influences around you (besides family, friends, work, etc.). After the 28 days of recording, you'll find you can predict your energy/moods and feelings, then use them to your benefit. (Some days more intuitive, some days more productive.)

See page 5 for the Energy of the Day reference chart.

Today's Galactic Body:

_____

What is the Energy of the Day today?

_____

What is the phase of the moon?

_____

What are today's colors?

_____

What is the element of your location?
(Earth, Air, Fire, Water)

_____

What is the weather today?
(Especially note extreme weather)

_____

How do you notice and respond to the Energy of the Day?
Draw, doodle, write, paste pictures/words.
Explore your way to express the Energy of the Day and perhaps your energy, too.

I chose this activity or activities to support my self-care today:

Week Four - Day Five

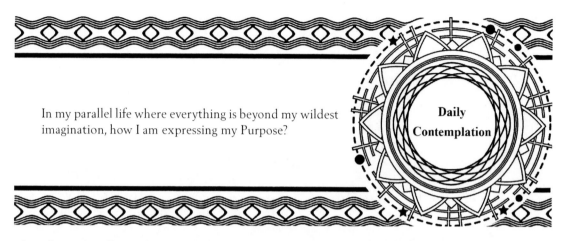

In my parallel life where everything is beyond my wildest imagination, how I am expressing my Purpose?

Daily Contemplation

Color, draw, doodle, and write about the above Daily Contemplation. Speak it out loud and to yourself to help internalize it. Include it in your daily meditation, walk or other practice. Notice when situations and circumstances arise where you can apply the Daily Contemplation.

What the Daily Contemplation Looks Like to Me:

How will you implement or integrate the Daily Contemplation today?

Week Four - Day Six

Day of the Week: _____   *Today's Date:* _____

To help clear your mind and ground your day,
color, draw, doodle, and play with this daily mandala...

Briefly write about how you noticed Purpose was active in your life yesterday

Week Four - Day Six

Intention: I see the Purpose in my life

Release the Mind From Clutter

What do I need to capture and then release from my mind, creating space so that I am open to possibilities?

Frustrations - Regrets - Sadness - Anger

Hopes – Dreams – Gratitude - Intentions

Plans – Want To's – Must Do's - Reminders

Draw, doodle, write, and do anything here for three minutes that helps clear your monkey-mind. Then, if you want, brainstorm ways to organize them into your life.

Week Four - Day Six

The Energy of the Day

Today, pay attention to all of the different elements and influences around you (besides family, friends, work, etc.). After the 28 days of recording, you'll find you can predict your energy/moods and feelings, then use them to your benefit. (Some days more intuitive, some days more productive.)

See page 5 for the Energy of the Day reference chart.

Today's Galactic Body:

_____

What is the phase of the moon?

_____

What is the element of your location?
(Earth, Air, Fire, Water)

_____

What is the Energy of the Day today?

_____

What are today's colors?

_____

What is the weather today?
(Especially note extreme weather)

_____

How do you notice and respond to the Energy of the Day?
Draw, doodle, write, paste pictures/words.
Explore your way to express the Energy of the Day and perhaps your energy, too.

I chose this activity or activities to support my self-care today:

Week Four - Day Six

I live Purposely in the mundane. (It could be while doing dishes, driving to the store; I am always in my Purpose even if it's not glamorous or fun.)

Daily Contemplation

Color, draw, doodle, and write about the above Daily Contemplation. Speak it out loud and to yourself to help internalize it. Include it in your daily meditation, walk or other practice. Notice when situations and circumstances arise where you can apply the Daily Contemplation.

What the Daily Contemplation Looks Like to Me:

How will you implement or integrate the Daily Contemplation today?

Week Four - Day Seven

Day of the Week: _____   *Today's Date:* _____

To help clear your mind and ground your day,
color, draw, doodle, and play with this daily mandala...

Briefly write about how you noticed Purpose was active in your life yesterday

Week Four - Day Seven

Intention: I see the Purpose in my life

Release the Mind From Clutter

*What do I need to capture and then release from my mind,
creating space so that I am open to possibilities?*

Frustrations - Regrets - Sadness - Anger

Hopes – Dreams – Gratitude - Intentions

Plans – Want To's – Must Do's - Reminders

Draw, doodle, write, and do anything here for three minutes that helps clear your monkey-mind.
Then, if you want, brainstorm ways to organize them into your life.

Week Four - Day Seven

The Energy of the Day

Today, pay attention to all of the different elements and influences around you (besides family, friends, work, etc.). After the 28 days of recording, you'll find you can predict your energy/ moods and feelings, then use them to your benefit. (Some days more intuitive, some days more productive.)

See page 5 for the Energy of the Day reference chart.

Today's Galactic Body:

_____

What is the phase of the moon?

_____

What is the element of your location?
(Earth, Air, Fire, Water)

_____

What is the Energy of the Day today?

_____

What are today's colors?

_____

What is the weather today?
(Especially note extreme weather)

_____

How do you notice and respond to the Energy of the Day?
Draw, doodle, write, paste pictures/words.
Explore your way to express the Energy of the Day and perhaps your energy, too.

I chose this activity or activities to support my self-care today:

Week Four - Day Seven

I honor myself.

Daily
Contemplation

Color, draw, doodle, and write about the above Daily Contemplation. Speak it out loud and to yourself to help internalize it. Include it in your daily meditation, walk or other practice. Notice when situations and circumstances arise where you can apply the Daily Contemplation.

What the Daily Contemplation Looks Like to Me:

How will you implement or integrate the Daily Contemplation today?

Week Four

Wrap-Up and Review

**Please reflect (looking back at your pages from this week)
and answer the following:**

In what ways has the energy shifted for you this week?

Do you notice patterns from day to day when clearing the clutter from your mind?

List the ways you are more in touch with your Purpose and note Ah Ha's moments you've gotten this week:

Journal and reflect on the energies of the day, the self-caren and other new habits you've created:

Week Four

Wrap-Up and Review

What are my top three Ah-Ha's from the past seven days?

1.

2.

3.

When was I the most proud in the past week?

Who have I served or loved this week as part of my Purpose?

How am I feeling about connecting with my Purpose?

28-Day Purpose

Wrap-Up and Review

Contemplate your weekly review pages and answer the following:

In what ways has the energy shifted for you these 28 days?

List the ways you are more in touch with your Purpose:

Journal and reflect on about how the energies have affected you over the past 28 days:

28-Day Purpose

Wrap-Up and Review

What are my top three Ah-Ha's from the past 28 days?

1.

2.

3.

When was I most proud, reflecting on these 28 days?

What is my commitment to myself moving forward?

28-Day Purpose

Wrap-Up and Review

Draw, doodle, color, cut and paste images of your Purpose

28-Day Purpose

Wrap-Up and Review

Write (a page) about your Purpose.
What it means to you and how you relate to Purpose.

SPARK Summary

Dear Fellow Human,

Congratulations! You've made it to the end of your 28-day journey. After you take a few days to rest your brain and allow yourself to integrate everything you've processed, it will be time to question what progress and success might mean to you.

Does success mean making money from your Purpose? If you believe that, then let that thought go. Connecting with your Purpose may not result in a different or immediate job change. It will, however, be connected to your work in the world. Often those are different and separate although sometimes they converge.

If you are not doing the work you believe you are meant to do (i.e. you're doing just doing a job), be careful not to subconsciously sabotage yourself. This may happen when we wish and hope for change, delivered sometimes in ways we didn't expect, like a layoff or illness. Honor the work you have now. It will evolve. Be brave, fearless; go for what you want and what you are meant to do, but without expectation. *That* is what often ends up holding us back. We become disappointed (again) and step back from ourselves because it 'never works out'... at least, not the way we projected.

The answer is to stop projecting negative energy. Set intentions. Be clear. Then, let it go. Move along to the next moment. Explore, create, serve, and Love. Be in your Purpose.

The next book in the series, *Intuition*, will guide you to discovering new ways to live your Purpose as well as listen to your guides, gut, and God. It will push, pull, and encourage you further along this journey. I'm here to support you.

In the meantime, take a few days; rest, relax, enjoy the break, and allow it to all integrate.

With Love,

Michelle

About Michelle A. Vandepas

Michelle here! I'm a Galactic Radically Mirrored Love Goddess, and sometimes get confused about my job here on Earth, but I'm committed to changing the planet for the best. My daughter (a Galactically overly-sensitive human herself) says I love my job, and I love being here as in be-ing here; I'm not confused about that. I'm doing what I know to do, best as I can, with full force while still be-ing in balance. What this means to me is working hard, resting hard, eating chocolate, drinking wine, walking, Qi-Gong, Tai Chi for meditation, jigsaw puzzles, chauffeuring my daughter, and whatever else crosses my path. When I have time, my favorite vacation spots include India, Honduras, and Florida.

For those who like to always know more, I am a Capricorn Manifesting Generator with a 3/5 and Right Angle Cross of The Vessel of Love. I have the Master number 22 in my birth-date. Life purpose number three and TheSpark.love is an eight. What does all this mean? Not much except they have all been nice validations over the years. Now I just set forth each day to live with Purpose, a bit of passion, a dash of wisdom, and pinch or more of fun.

And what I love comes through in how I "be" in my doing. I'm a bestselling author and TEDx speaker. I work with those who need a bigger audience, have a message to share, and know that now is the time. I've been a successful business consultant, started three multimillion-dollar companies, produced a documentary, and have been an advisor to top-level business people, politicians, and already visible coaches as well as authors. I have been filmed for the documentary "Wisdom from Thought Leaders," along with Sting and the Dalai Lama. With my Doctor of Divinity, I bring a spiritual bent to my work.

I've been married 35 years (!), have a joyful daughter, am grandmother to six, and have been a foster mom to ten. I help people every day identify authentically, see their paths to making an impact, and empowering them to make a difference in our world through training, speaking, and coaching as well as working with Authors, Practitioners, and those who have a calling. People sharing their success is the strongest testimony available. I invite you to consider your Purpose, your Passion, and how we can make an impact together.

What's Next? INTUITION

This is an excerpt from the next book in SPARK: The Radically Authentic Life series:
INTUITION: The Alignment Guide

Time is bending backward on itself. The veil seems torn. I feel it, and I know you feel it, too. The energy is crazy, busy, hectic, and wild; even when we escape into nature, the extreme weather hits, or we get to experience an eclipse! There are times I feel like I'm living in the Twilight Zone whereas other times it's the Dr. Who/Star Trek ripped time/space continuum.

Intuitively, we know we need to slow down and listen, both deeply to ourselves as well as that inner voice. We can hear our intuitive voice, but we don't always respond appropriately. It's difficult to discern if it's our mind or intuition or emotion or our long lost friend in our brain telling us what to do (or shouldn't do). We aren't always sure where our intuition lives and how to access it when we need it most.

Does it reside in our gut or solar plexus? Do we feel it as a tingling in our hands? Is it a sense of something 12 degrees to the right of your left ear and it feeds you info? All of these are true, but probably only one is true for you. Do you know which it is?

It's hard to tell because we cram more and more into our days to the point of distraction where we aren't able to hear the very quiet whispers of our intuitive selves. Since we have instant access to everything now, and we are always getting what we want NOW, there is never a moment to stop, reflect, and be in peace. There is no delayed gratification, the information never stops. It comes to us through a fire hose, and when our guidance comes, it's drowned silent. Besides, who has time to be intuitive?

I remember life without a cell phone, but now I can't imagine it. There is so much freedom in being able to find the nearest restaurant, to get directions, or to see where Yemen is on a map in relationship to Egypt. However, instant access, instant news, instant gratification pushes us forward until there is no downtime, no place inside to relax—our mind never turns off. It just keeps gushing at us, more more more. When we are in GO mode, we become more anxious and pull away from our body as well as our intuition, yet this is the exact time we need to be more connected!

What's Next? INTUITION

On the flip side, I also notice that at times life slows to microseconds. We see things we haven't previously noticed. We do double-takes when the world seems tiny, and we meet our neighbor on a train halfway around the world. What does it mean? What can our intuition tell us about these events?

The extreme weather and other events worldwide have us all on alert, traumatized. Most teenagers I know have some form of high anxiety. Parenting, while addressing so many catastrophic issues, is triggering all the moms I know. Is it even possible to stay safe?

Some say the Total Eclipse took us back to 1998 to clean up our past, release any lingering triggers, or traumas—yet we are continually triggered and traumatized. With the perpetual instant feedback, there is no time to process the give-and-take of life. When we create an action, the reactions are immediate. Instant Karma is happening. The way to move forward in this state of hyper-energy is to retreat inside, pay attention, say no to a lot of noise, grab a moment of silence, and listen for our intuition. When we are quiet, only then can we hear it speak. Then we must move forward throughout the day, making choices based on who we are, and take action based on what is true for us. We can hear the calls.

Being connected with our intuition doesn't mean we don't make choices that seem 'wrong' or take wrong turns. Life won't suddenly be a bed of roses. However, I know that when we navigate the best we can, moment by moment, knowing we are conscious, alert and connected, then we hear what isn't being said aloud. When we are open and listening, the synchronicities happen quickly. Magic abounds. We manifest (in both good and bad ways, as in 'be careful what you ask for'). We learn to ride the wave rather than be swept into it. Calm and collected. Ready.

But how do we do this?

Listening. Quietly. Learning what our bodies tell us. Intuition lives in our physical bodies; it might show up as a tingling or a feeling. Most of us know it, but the understanding often comes in hindsight. "I should have listened to myself" or "I knew that would happen."

The pages that follow will assist you in aligning more with your intuition so that you can recognize it while it happens, not just interpret the confirmation later.

What's Next? INTUITION

These activities will force you to slow down for a few moments each day and notice what your body tells you. Being in this space will help you to discern what is trauma, negative emotion, or bad food. What, in fact, is intuition? It's time to listen more closely. Our intuitive self depends upon it.

Go here to preorder Intuition: The Alignment Guide:
https://thespark.love/intuition-the-alignment-guide/
and, while you are there remember to get your gifts and discounts.

Hang on tight!

Michelle